Pom Pom

by
Louis Schutter
and
Norma Youngberg

(Story material from "Buck" Weaver)
Newly-updated section by Ed Guthero

This is a newly-revised edition of the original book *Pom Pom*. It includes an additional updated chapter complete with many photos from Buck Weaver's popular *Buckaroo 500* children's television show.

This book is dedicated to and in memory of :
Ted "Tater" Weaver (father), 1901–1998
Ethel Weaver (mother), 1910–1999
Joan R. Weaver (wife), 1931–2001

CONTENTS

"Don't forget to do your best always! . . . and don't miss church, ever!"— *Buck*

CHAPTER 1

Kathy's Horses

The Weavers' Boys' Ranch nestled among glistening patches of new snow. Light curls of smoke from the ranch house chimney spiraled into the cloudy sky as though eager to welcome the fresh fall of flakes.

No one could imagine that twenty-two boys lived, and worked, and played in and about the old ranch house. A quiet calm lay over the rolling Nevada desert. Even the herd of pure-bred Hereford cattle chewed their cuds as they stood about in the fence corners looking drowsy and content.

Inside the ranch house living room, Kathy Weaver turned her back on the fire in the stone fireplace and stared out the low-silled window toward the open pasture land. Not often was the big house so empty. This afternoon the nineteen ranch boys and her two older brothers worked at a special job, building partitions in the barn. Only Timmie her third brother, the one next older than she, sprawled on the davenport with a book in his hand.

Through the thick fall of snow, Kathy could just make out the mailbox and the mail-carrier's car as he stopped in front of it.

"I'm going for the mail," Kathy sang out as she pulled a stocking cap over her dark curls and shrugged into a leather jacket.

Out in the drive, she scuffed through the deep whiteness

and lifted her face to the falling snow. She spread her unmittened hand to catch the flakes and laughed aloud as she danced along the drive. At the sound of her laughter her small black dog, Jet, came racing after her and she stooped to pet him.

Then she remembered something — Daddy's face at breakfast time. He had answered the phone and when he came back to the table that worried expression had fastened itself on his face. Kathy had felt something sharp and heavy turn in her middle. What could make Daddy look like that? Right after breakfast, he had driven off in the old pickup.

She still stroked Jet's soft fur, but the laughter died in her throat. She slowed her steps to a dragged-out pace and reached the mailbox at last.

"Mostly magazines," she drew the bundle of papers and letters from the box and tucked them under her jacket. She handed a folded advertisement to Jet, who took the paper between his teeth and marched beside her toward the house.

At the ranch house door she rapped sharply.

Tim appeared.

"Here, Timmie, take this mail in. I must sweep the snow off my feet." She gave her brother the bundle and reached for an old broom that leaned against the porch railing. With slow and thoughtful strokes, she swept the snow from her shoes. Then she took the paper from Jet's mouth, thanked him and called him a good dog. She told him how cozy the barn must be right now, and urged him to run along and see what the boys were doing out there. Jet ran off.

Back in the living room, Kathy bent over the pile of mail which still lay where Tim had dumped it, on the library table.

"Oh look, Timmie," she pointed to the top magazine where the picture of a white horse decorated the back cover.

Tim looked up from his book. "I suppose you're going to cut it out."

Kathy had already reached for the scissors. "Of course I'm going to cut it out. This horse is exactly what I want for my scrapbook cover. I've been looking for a good picture of a white horse."

Tim watched her make the first cut. "You know Daddy doesn't like reading clipped magazines."

"He won't mind. It's a horse picture."

"I don't think he'll like it." Tim picked up Kathy's scrapbook and leafed through it, looking at all the horse pictures Kathy had pasted in neat arrangements through two-thirds of the big pages.

"You've sure got a lot of horse pictures." He laid the book down and Kathy brought her jar of paste. Before she centered the white horse on the green scrapbook cover, she held it up to admire the graceful shape.

The day seemed to brighten. Kathy looked toward the window and saw that the snow had stopped falling and the setting sun shone through between the clouds. Bright rays fell on the picture and threw a shadow on the floor — the silhouette of a horse with long, long legs, a horse many times larger than the paper horse Kathy held in her hand.

"Oh look, Timmie." Kathy tipped the horse this way and that until the shadow seemed to come alive. It pranced and stretched itself into grotesque figures on the floor.

"A Houdini horse!" Tim laughed. "Now he's white: now he's black. What kind of trick is this?"

"Just look at his shape," Kathy held the paper horse out to her brother, "perfect body, perfect head, perfect lines . . . "

Tim interrupted her. "I never saw anyone so crazy about horses." Tim glanced out the window at the sinking sun. "Come on out and help me milk. Pretend the cow is a horse."

"Oh great! wouldn't she look charming with a saddle?"

Tim threw down his book, got up and stretched. "You just bet she'd look fine with a saddle. You could thread the reins through her horns — nothing like spurring for milk."

He took down the milk bucket and both children put on warm caps and jackets. Together they skipped out of the house and down the path to the barn where the Holstein cow and her calf waited to get in. Tim opened the barn door and called the cow.

Kathy thrust one tine of the pitchfork into a bale of hay and twisted it to break the wire. The bale burst open and the fragrance of cured alfalfa filled the barn. She forked several bunches into the manger.

While Tim scattered straw on the damp floor and fastened the cow's head in the stanchion, Kathy brought the three-legged stool.

"Push this calf into the next stall where her mother can reach over and lick her." Tim balanced himself on the milk stool.

With the calf out of the way, he began to milk. Kathy leaned on the pitchfork and watched him.

"Timmie," Kathy couldn't keep the worry out of her voice. "Did you see Daddy's face when he drove away right after breakfast?"

"No, guess I was out feeding the chickens."

"Someone called on the phone and Daddy had such a worried look when he came back to the breakfast table. Then he took off in the pickup right after he'd eaten. He looked so unhappy, it . . . well, I just can't forget it."

Tim sighed. "Must be something about money again. It sure takes a lot of dough to run this outfit. Seems as though there's never enough of anything."

"Wonder what we could do to help." Kathy felt sure that if she and her brothers could only think hard enough they could figure out some way to make money.

Tim bent to his milking and the streams of milk sang against the sides of the pail as foam rose higher and higher. "One way you might help, is to quit teasing Daddy every morning and every evening to get you a horse."

"Oh, Timmie, you know I want a real live horse more than anything else in the world. Of course I'd want a horse that could earn money, you know, pay for himself. Surely there must be ways a horse can make money."

Tim leaned back and laughed until the cow turned her head a little to look at him and jerked back in a reckless effort to pull her head out of the stanchion.

Tim grabbed the milk bucket from under the cow's feet and began stripping the last milk from her teats. "That calf has sucked herself plum full this day."

Tim stood up with the half-filled bucket in his hand. He held it out for his sister to see. "Look, how far do you think that'll go among twenty-five people?"

"Guess Daddy will have to pen the calf up in the corral, else none of us will have any milk tomorrow."

Kathy couldn't get the horse out of her mind. "Really, Timmie, I mean it. Isn't there some way a horse can make money?"

"Oh, I suppose race horses might make money, if they're good enough; but you know Daddy wouldn't go for horse-racing."

Kathy looked longingly over at the empty stall beyond the one where the calf was penned. Every time she looked at that stall, her imagination put a horse there, a beautiful horse with a high arched neck, graceful legs and a kind face.

She checked herself with the thought of Daddy. Trouble had really got hold of him today, not just ordinary worries. She knew it must be worse this time, something especially bad.

Tim opened the stanchion and the cow headed for the open door, calling to her calf as she lumbered along.

"I'm not turning that calf loose yet." Tim shoved on the cow's hind-quarters to hurry her out the door. "I think when Dad sees how little milk we got tonight, he'll keep that calf penned away from her mother for good."

"Seems as though everything gets less and less." Kathy drove the pitchfork into an unopened bale of hay with more force than she needed to use. "Less food, less clothes, less driving so's to save gas and oil, and now less . . . ."

Tim spoke in a sharp voice. "Hold it, Kathy. When Daddy and Mother started this boys' ranch, they knew it wouldn't be easy. Remember, they told us kids we'd have to make sacrifices and we all agreed."

"I remember." Kathy felt ashamed. "And every one of the boys has gotten better since he came to live on our ranch, every one of the nineteen."

Tim seemed to be thinking hard. "You know I heard the bookkeeper say yesterday that the ranch is in the red"

"Maybe he meant that the buildings need new paint."

"Don't be silly, Kathy. The buildings need new paint all right, but that isn't what he meant. Our expenses are more than our income. That's what he meant. You're good at arithmetic."

At the kitchen door, Mother took the milk from Tim and strained it. "Not much milk tonight," she said.

"No, the calf got it."

Supper waited on the long table. Most of the twenty-three boys gathered round it had already emptied their soup bowls, and started on the huge platter of hot cornbread.

Kathy looked at Daddy's empty chair at the head of the table. "Where's Daddy? Isn't he home yet?"

Mother ladled out soup for Kathy and Tim. "He phoned to say he'd be busy with the bookeeper for a while yet and may not be home until late."

"He won't get any supper and he . . ." Again Kathy felt that uncomfortable twinge of worry and a dull pain. Poor Daddy!

"No, he won't get a hot supper and he had no lunch either." Mother's usually pleasant face looked troubled. "He must have been terribly busy today."

Kathy bent over her bowl of soup. In spite of her distracted mind, she felt hungry. "Please pass the horse — I mean the salt."

Tim shouted with laughter and all the other boys at the table joined in with howls of merriment. Kathy felt her cheeks burn.

"I never did see such a horse-crazy kid," Mike, her eldest brother, remarked as he speared himself another chunk of cornbread.

After supper, Kathy helped Mother with the dishes, then went to find Tim. "Timmie, will you play horse with me?"

Chuck, Kathy's second brother looked in the door and overheard their talk. "Well, I see you'll be whinnying the rest of the evening." He backed out and went to join the other boys.

"Sure, I'll play horse with you." Tim laid down the *Farm Journal* with its back page missing. "Bring out your horses."

Kathy made three trips to her bedroom closet and brought back, at each trip, a basket full of toy horses, glass horses, porcelain horses, plastic horses, metal horses, flocked horses with plushy coats, every kind of toy horse Kathy had been able to collect over nine years of horse-loving and horse-longing.

The two children spread the horses in front of the fire. "What shall we play tonight?" Tim matched a pair of ginger-colored ponies. "Shall we have a race?"

Kathy hesitated a minute. Daddy's worried face stood out clear in her mind and even the prospect of a horse game with Tim could not take away the sadness. "Let's play church," she said.

"All right. Who'll preach?"

Kathy picked up her favorite stuffed horse made of brown felt. She smoothed his long silky tail. "Seven-up will preach." She set the stuffed horse on the raised brick hearth in front of the fireplace.

"We'll need a choir, too." Tim began sorting out all the black and white horses. He set them in rows below Seven-up and a little to one side, "See, they have on their black and white choir robes."

Kathy laughed, then felt a little guilty. Somehow it seemed wrong to laugh and have fun when Daddy acted so worried and sad.

Seven-up preached a fine sermon in Tim's voice and the congregation showed perfect respect and reverence. Not one of them moved.

"I'm going to bed," Kathy said as the sermon ended. She began to pick up the horses and load them into the basket.

"So soon?" Tim looked surprised.

"I don't feel good," Kathy told him. "I think I'm getting a fever."

With all the horses returned to their closet shelves, Kathy sat on the edge of her bed and looked fondly at them all. She went over and picked Seven-up from the middle shelf and closed the closet door. She laid the stuffed horse on her bed. Then she turned out the light, cuddled Seven-up in her arms and lay down with her face toward the window that looked out on the driveway. She wanted to watch for the headlights of Daddy's pickup when it turned into the drive.

"I love you, Seven-up," she whispered. "You aren't as pretty as you used to be. Your seams are split, one eye is lost, and you need a bath, but I still love you. Probably you are the only real horse I'm ever going to have."

A long time later, she saw the pickup's lights and heard Daddy's voice in the kitchen. She knew Mother would be warming a late supper for him right now. She didn't feel sleepy at all and for quite a while she lay there between the warm quilts, thinking.

She wanted to see Daddy's face now. Maybe he would look happy again as he always did when things were going well. She slid out of bed and crept down to the kitchen door with Seven-up clasped in her arms.

The kitchen seemed unusually quiet. Of course the late supper must be over by now, but a light showed under the door. Daddy and Mother must be in there still. She pushed the door open a crack and pressed her bare foot against it.

Yes, Daddy and Mother were there all right. They knelt in prayer beside the kitchen table. The ache in her middle turned into a lump that pushed up in her throat until she gasped for breath, but softly so they wouldn't hear. She heard Daddy's voice low and trembling:

Help us, Dear Lord, for we can't help ourselves

through this trouble. Don't let us lose the ranch.

Don't let our boys go hungry . . .

Kathy didn't wait to hear more. She couldn't choke back the sob that just would burst out. She ran back to her room.

With Seven-up in her arms, she slept at last while round the Weaver Ranch house the snow drifted, cold and silent.

CHAPTER 2

More Trouble

Kathy wakened to see the glimmer of moonlight on new-fallen snow outside her window and she heard Mother's voice calling, "Wake up Kathy. It's six o'clock."

Kathy hurried into her clothes, for the unheated bedroom felt chilly. She pulled on her flannel-lined jeans and drew a long-sleeved pullover on over her blouse.

In the kitchen, she found Mother stuffing wadded paper and kindling into the old range. Flames caught and flared. Kathy held her cold hands out to the warmth.

Mother filled a kettle with water from the copper reservoir, water still a little warm from yesterday's fire.

"This reservoir is almost empty. We mustn't forget to fill it." Mother spread a blue and white checked tablecloth on the long table and Kathy set on the dishes and laid the silverware.

"Go bring me some oatmeal, Kathy; this water is almost boiling." Mother salted the water.

In the pantry, Kathy took a carton of oatmeal from the storage shelf. "Last box, Mother." She set it on the table. "Will this one be enough?"

Mother opened the carton and looked in. "No, it won't be enough. I'll have to use what's here and then stir up some hot-cakes. Good thing some of the boys don't care much for oatmeal." She stirred the oatmeal from the carton into the

15

boiling water and set it on the back of the stove to simmer.

Kathy went to the sink to fill a pitcher with water for the reservoir. She turned on the faucet but no water came. Spitting, sputtering noises came out. Burps and coughs shook the faucet.

"No water?" Mother came to look. "Pipes must be frozen, or maybe that pump's conked out again." She turned the faucet off and on several times — no water.

"Go call Daddy, hurry, Kathy!"

Kathy ran to the bedroom. "Wake up, Daddy." She roused him from a sound sleep. "Wake up quick! We've got no water to make breakfast. Hurry!"

When Daddy examined the rebellious faucet, he shook his head, stepped outside to look at the thermometer on the back porch and came back inside still shaking his head. "Thirty-four degrees on the back porch — not cold enough to freeze water in the pipes. It's that pump again."

Mother thrust the big dishpan at Kathy and put a shallow bowl in her hand. Kathy and Daddy went out the kitchen door together. Daddy headed for the pump house while Kathy began to skim the softest, whitest snow from the newly-made drifts. She filled the dishpan, heaped it and pressed the snow down into it with the bowl. She carried it to Mother who set it over the fire. As soon as it began to melt, she pored off water and stirred up the hotcake batter. By the time Daddy came back from the pump house, hotcakes sizzled on the griddle and sugar syrup boiled in a saucepan.

"Did you get the pump fixed, Daddy?"

"No, Honey." He turned to Mother. "Something's wrong with the pump motor, I think. The thing's too hot to touch."

"You'd better call the pump man right away." Mother began to dish up the oatmeal and piled a couple platters with hotcakes. "Kathy, call the boys to breakfast."

Daddy went to the telephone.

The cluster of Weavers and the nineteen ranch boys swarmed in and devoured the oatmeal and hotcakes in far less time than it had taken to prepare them. The boys made jokes about the "snowcakes" and "frost syrup."

"This snow meal isn't bad. Please snowball me the sleet syrup and the icicle milk," Mike cracked.

Daddy came back from the telephone and sat down in his place. Kathy looked at him. He wasn't smiling. He looked even more worried than he had yesterday.

A knock on the door silenced everyone. Tim ran to let the visitor in. The pump man walked into the room. He rubbed his hands together and held them over the range to warm. Mother invited him to have some breakfast, but he refused.

"I sure do hate ta tell ya, but yer pump's burnt out, coils, armatures, everything. I just went and looked at it." He frowned and shrugged his shoulders. "No use ya foolin' with a mess o' junk like that. Better get ya a new one or a good rebuilt job." He seemed to be studying Daddy's drawn face. "Tell ya what I'll do, Weaver. I'll let ya have a new pump wholesale, same price I pay."

"How much?" Daddy's voice came out low, but steady.

"A pump like the one ya got costs $150. I'll let ya have a new one at shop invoice price, $100.

Kathy saw Daddy wince and his shoulders sagged like an old man's. "Hope my credit's good with you," Daddy said. "I haven't the money to pay you but we must have water."

"Sure, sure, o-kay. We'll bill ya and ya can have till the tenth of next month."

"Put it in. Put it in this morning." Daddy's face and the desperate look in his eyes struck Kathy like a blow. Today was the 26th. How could Daddy possibly get a hundred dollars by the 10th of next month?

When the pump man had gone, Kathy looked around at the boys still sitting at the bare breakfast table. Not a morsel of food remained, yet they still sat in their places and they all looked serious.

Peter whispered something to Mack, the biggest and strongest of the ranch boys. Then he turned to Daddy. "Dad Weaver, supposing you let us fellows help you pay that bill for the pump? Let us give a program, or a concert, or something."

Kathy thought the sad lines in Daddy's face softened a little. "That's a fine idea, Peter." Daddy got up from the table. "I'll think it over and see what I can suggest. The Lion's Club has asked me to speak to them sometime soon. Maybe I'd better call the president and make a date to give them a speech." He grinned for the first time in two days. "They usually give us fifty dollars to help our work here on the ranch."

"Let us boys put on something extra for them." Peter had gotten to his feet, too. "We can get up a good program, betcha they give you a hundred dollars this time. That'll take care of the pump."

Kathy jumped up and ran to Daddy. She threw her arms around his neck and said loudly into his ear. "Oh, that will be great fun, Daddy. Let me help get up the program. I can do lots of tricks."

"That you can." Daddy laughed. "It's a deal. I'll call the Lion's Club president and tell him what we're cooking up."

"That puts an idea into my head," Mother spoke up. "Maybe I could make some kind of a treat for the Lion's Club."

Daddy seemed enthusiastic, for a minute his face looked as happy as it usually did. "Tell you what we'll do," he said. "We'll invite them out here to the ranch. You can serve them some of your wholloping good nut-rolls and hot chocolate and we can show them what we're doing here on the Weavers' Boys' Ranch. They can see the carpenter shop, the barn, the farm, the pure-bred cattle . . . ."

Mother interrupted him. "Perhaps the boys will perform better here at home, too. They won't feel strange."

Peter took charge at once. "Mack, you can give that funny reading about the old maid and her sick cow. Chuck, you can get up a quartette and Tim can speak his piece about the boy that 'chonked green apples' and got the stomach ache."

"I guess the boys could all sing together in a chorus." Daddy seemed to be caught up in the boys' enthusiasm. "that is, all who can carry a tune."

Every boy admitted in a loud voice that he could certainly carry a tune.

By evening, Daddy had spoken to the Lion's Club president and invited them to visit the ranch the next Tuesday afternoon. All the Club members would be delighted to come, the president had said.

Tremendous enthusiasm possessed everyone in the big ranch house. All the boys wanted to help. Those who could not recite poems could do tricks like standing on their heads, or rolling along like cartwheels. All over the farm, boys practised songs, poems, speeches, and tricks to audiences of Herefords, hens and calves.

Mother made costumes for the boys who meant to act out a charade. She sewed a new pink ruffly dress for Kathy who intended to represent a rose in a poem Mike wanted to recite.

"What can we use for decorations?" Kathy asked Mother. "There are no flowers in winter and all the pretty grasses and leaves and shrubs that grow out here in the desert are buried under the snow drifts."

Mother thought for a while. "It would be nice to have some pretty decorations. The boys would like that, too. I tell you what, Kathy, we can use walnuts. We can kill two birds with one stone."

"How can we use walnuts, Mother. They aren't very bright or pretty."

"We'll make them bright and pretty. You'll see." Mother dragged the big bag of walnuts from the store room and emptied a lot of them into a flat basket. "You must be careful and crack them so the halves of the shells do not break. We will use the meats for our rolls and the shells for our decorations."

Keeping the walnut halves from breaking took a lot of patience, but Kathy's curiosity made her so eager to see what Mother intended to make from the shells that she didn't mind the work at all.

At last a big pan of perfect walnut halves stood on the kitchen table. "Now what?" Kathy asked.

"I think we have both gold and silver metal paint in the pantry. Go look on the top shelf."

Kathy came back with two bottles. Each bottle had a soft little brush fastened to it.

"Now brush the walnut shells with either gold or silver paint." Mother showed Kathy how, "Put them on newspapers to dry with the round side up. They will dry in a few minutes."

The gilding went fast and doing it turned out to be fun. The big table and the sink drain-boards soon filled up with rows of gold and silver walnut shells.

"Now, while those shells dry, go and bring my piece-bag from the stair closet." Kathy ran after it.

She watched Mother dump the contents of the big gunny bag on the kitchen floor.

"Now, pick out pieces of bright colored velvet or silk. They need not be large. Small pieces are best — the kind we can cut into circles about the size of a small teacup."

They picked out red, green, orange, lilac, blue and pink bits of silk, satin and velvet. Kathy's curiosity grew by the minute. She still had no idea what magic Mother would use to make these common walnut shells into decorations fancy enough for the Lion's Club.

Last of all, Mother brought out a bundle of fluffy cotton and a bunch of blue, pink, and yellow baby-ribbon which she cut into odd lengths. Then Kathy watched her cover small balls of cotton with the bright scraps of silk and velvet. Then she pressed the balls into the glittering walnut shells. Into the stem end of each, Mother glued a length of baby ribbon.

Kathy clapped her hands and capered around the kitchen in a dance of joy. "Oh, Mother, they are beautiful!"

When each walnut had been stuffed with a fat little stomach of brilliant color, Mother gathered them into clusters with ribbons of uneven length. Some of them hung down a couple feet and others dangled on very short lengths of ribbon.

"I think we have some yellow crepe paper around here somewhere," Mother said. "We can make some fancy bows to tie these clusters up where we want them."

Later, Kathy stood looking up at the clusters of dangling walnut halves. They hung from the ceiling rafters and over the stone fireplace. The room looked fit for the president. Daddy himself said so.

On Monday, Mother and Kathy scrubbed floors and arranged comfortable chairs to seat the guests.

"This room looks simply lovely, Mother." Kathy said for the twentieth time. "Those clusters of walnuts look like something real precious."

Early Tuesday morning, Mother set a huge batch of rolls to rise. By the time the Lion's Club members began to arrive, the fragrance of cinnamon and baking bread filled the house.

Twenty-two boys, scrubbed and combed, dressed in clean shirts and jeans, chewed their fingernails and wriggled in their chairs waiting for Dad Weaver to make his speech.

Kathy hadn't thought much about horses the last two days, but when the boys got up to stumble through their pieces, the idea occurred to her that a horse could do much better.

Poor as the performances were, in Kathy's critical opinion, the Lion's Club clapped their hands with wild enthusiasm and Kathy felt sure they were pleased with the boys' foolishness as well as by Mother's delicious rolls and hot chocolate. Kathy reasoned, if they usually gave Daddy fifty dollars, they would surely give him more this time.

Early darkness had fallen when the men left and the family settled down before the open fire to rest and talk. Kathy sat on the floor and dreamed about horses. Again she thought how much nicer the afternoon's program would have been had a horse been doing the tricks instead of those clumsy boys.

Part of Kathy's mind wandered in green summer pastures with the dream horse she longed to own, but another part of her brain listened to everything that went on around her.

She heard Daddy and Mother talking somewhere in the room. She did not turn to see where they sat, but fixed her eyes on the fire in the big stone fireplace.

She heard Mother ask, "How much did the Lion's Club give you this time, Dear?"

"Nothing," she heard Daddy's answer clearly. Although he spoke in a whisper, Kathy heard.

Nothing? Nothing. So that's how all their hard work and great plans had turned out! Now that the Lion's Club had seen what good things the Weavers had to eat — now that they knew how delicious Mother's walnut rolls and hot chocolate tasted. Now that they had seen what lovely decorations the Weavers could afford to have hanging from the rafters in the big living room, it must be they had decided that the Weavers were rich and didn't need a thing. Nothing — nothing!

"S'posed to be a three-year old Welsh . . . He'll sell for a thousand dollars, too."

CHAPTER 3

A Horse

Kathy turned on her pillow and listened. Someone stirred somewhere in the big ranch house. Her keen ears told her that Mother must be up already and building the fire. Why hadn't Mother come to call her as she usually did?

Something dark and ugly tugged at the back of Kathy's mind — some burden she must get under before the new day began. Ah yes, now the thing came forward and settled over her like a cloud. The Lion's Club had spent yesterday afternoon and evening at the ranch. They had listened to Daddy's fine speech and enjoyed the boys' poems and readings. They had clapped for the fancy tricks and they had all eaten Mother's rolls and sipped her delicious hot chocolate. Then they had gone away without giving Daddy one single cent.

Kathy dragged out of bed and hunted for her jeans and shirt. Now how would Daddy pay for that pump? Would the pump man come and take it away? The hundred dollars must be paid by next week and now Daddy couldn't pay it. Mother knew how much she worried about such things. That must be why she hadn't called.

The smell of fried potatoes and onions welcomed Kathy at the kitchen door. Mother stood over the big black skillet and sizzling noises filled the air.

"Come, Kathy, I'm so glad you're up." Mother handed her the big putty knife she always used for turning fried potatoes.

"Please keep turning them. We want them golden brown, not black."

Mother opened the oven door and Kathy saw that a baked omelet rose golden and fluffy in the dripping-pan.

"Watch the omelet, too," Mother said. "It's almost done. You know it has to come out at exactly the right second."

Kathy knew. She knew all about burned potatoes and fallen omelets. She had watered such failures with her tears often enough so that now she knew she could be trusted to manage breakfast as well as Mother could.

"I think I'll cut these left-over rolls in two; then there'll be a enough to go around and each boy can have a little piece to go with his hot chocolate."

Twenty-two boys followed their noses into the kitchen and took their usual places. Everyone sat in silence for a moment. Daddy's chair was vacant. Where could he have gone so early in the morning?

Mother asked Chuck to offer thanks, and he repeated the same prayer he had said since he first sat up to the table. Then, like well-handled soldiers, the boys all began to eat.

"Where's Daddy?" Tim asked.

"Someone called him late last night and he went into town early this morning." Mother served the boys second helpings.

"Who was it?" Chuck asked between bites of omelet.

"I don't know," Mother answered. "I had already gone to bed and dropped off to sleep. The phone woke me up partly. Guess I must have been pretty tired. Daddy left before I wakened this morning.

"You know," Peter held a fork full of fried potatoes in mid-air. "Three or four of those Lion's Club members wore striped suits. They look more like tigers than lions."

"The way that one in the tan suit growled and snarled when he talked, he could have been a lion all right." Mack jiggled Peter's hand so that the potatoes fell back into his plate.

"I liked the president," Kathy chirped up. "He is so nice and handsome; but that other man, the treasurer, I didn't like him. He looked mean and ugly. I know he is the treasurer, because Daddy pointed him out to me. He's not only mean and ugly; he's stingy, too!"

"Why Kathy, that's no way to talk about any person. If you can't speak well of a man, hold your tongue." Mother looked stern.

"I don't care. It's true." Kathy banged her fork on her empty plate. "It's all his fault that the Lion's Club didn't give Daddy any money." Kathy's voice rose higher and higher. "They all raved about the delicious rolls and the hot chocolate; they 'oh-ed and ah-ed' over the ranch. They clapped like crazy over the boys' stupid tricks, but did old Mister Stingy Pockets cough up one single red cent? He did not! He could have helped us, but he didn't do a thing!" She was so upset her eyes glowed like hot coals.

Mother took hold of Kathy's shoulder and shook her. "Kathy, get it out of your head that we are kind to people so they will give us money. Do you know Who we depend on for everything? Have you forgotten? You make me ashamed."

Kathy hung her head.

Mother's face looked angry. "Do you know, Kathy, that we are not permitted to speak rudely of any person, because everyone belongs to God and all are equally dear to Him?"

"I'm sorry, Mother," Kathy said. "I guess I feel disappointed that we can't pay for the pump after all, and you know how it worries Daddy."

Kathy got up from the table and checked the oven and the skillet to make sure that Daddy would have some breakfast. "I guess that program wasn't really so good. Daddy's speech sounded wonderful, and the food tasted delicious. Of course, if we'd had a trained horse. . . ."

"I knew it! I knew it!" Mike slapped his knee with a loud whack. "If we could get through a single meal without a horse at the table, the dishes would cry out with withdrawal pains."

Kathy whirled toward him. "I don't care what you. . . .!"

The kitchen door burst open and Daddy seemed to take a

flying leap into the middle of the room. He held something in his right hand. Kathy couldn't make out what it was. He waved it over his head.

"A check, everybody, a check!"

"From the Lion's Club?" Kathy screamed the question. "Is it for a hundred dollars?"

"Guess again."

"The boys shouted, $150, $200, $250?"

Daddy still stood waving the check with that huge grin on his face. "Where is your faith, people, where is your faith? This check is for $300!"

The boys loosed such a hub-bub of clapping and stomping and cheering that Kathy couldn't make herself heard for at least two minutes. She took hold of Daddy's free hand and clung to it.

When he finally silenced the boys, Kathy dove into the silence like a pearl fisherman into a fresh oyster bed. "Oh Daddy, we can pay for the pump and have enough left to buy a horse."

Mike and Chuck threw up their hands and pretended to faint.

"Honey, we couldn't do that. It wouldn't be right to use the money that way. The Lion's Club intends for us to use this extra money for things we actually need for the ranch like food, clothing, supplies, lumber — things of that sort. Two hundred dollars isn't enough to buy much of a horse, certainly not a horse that can be trained to do tricks."

"But Daddy," Kathy's mind did a quick somersault. "Wouldn't a horse be sort of an investment? I've heard you say that wise investments are the same as money in the bank, or something like that."

Daddy didn't answer. He stared at the floor as though trying to solve some problem. Maybe she could persuade him on this horse idea. She wouldn't give up — no, never, no matter how much the boys teased her, and made fun of her horse plans.

Mother set a warmed-over breakfast on the table. Daddy tucked the check inside his wallet and sat down to a hearty meal. The boys all excused themselves and went outside to start their delayed chores.

When Daddy finished eating, he hurried out to the car and drove off again.

"Where did he go now?" Kathy asked Mother as they cleared the breakfast table.

"Back to town, I guess. Said he had some important business."

"Oh Mother, do you think he's gone to get a horse?" The thought almost took Kathy's breath away. "You do think the horse is a good idea, don't you, Mother?"

"I think the horse is a wonderful idea, but a horse is so expensive. You see, Kathy, a horse that could be trained to do tricks well enough to make money costs a lot, maybe more than we could possibly pay."

Mother and Kathy were making sandwiches for lunch when Daddy came back with a big box of groceries. Kathy ran to open the door for him. "Did you get the horse?"

"No, Honey, I didn't get one, but I did look at one — a black Shetland pony, a real beauty."

"Oh let me go and see it, Daddy. Let's go right now." She flung off her apron.

"Now wait just a minute, Kathy." Daddy set down the heavy box. "Before we go, I must explain to you that this pony costs $1000. Even if the horse-trader could let me have it for less, we still couldn't raise the money. $1000 is a pile of money, Kathy."

"Did you tell the horse-trader we'd take the pony, Daddy?"

"No, of course I didn't. I couldn't promise to take any pony when I know I can't pay for it." Daddy looked thoughtfully at Kathy for a moment. "And I'm not sure it's a good thing for me to take you over there. You may be disappointed."

"Oh I want to see that pony, Daddy." Kathy grabbed her warm jacket and cap from the hook on the kitchen wall. "Even if we can't buy it, I want to see it."

"All right, I guess you're old enough to take a little disappointment. You are bound to have plenty later on in life." Daddy opened the door. "Remember we are only shopping around for a horse. And don't forget that we have no thousand dollars to pay for anything."

Kathy sat on the edge of the pickup seat straining forward as though she could make the pickup go faster. A black Shetland pony! Maybe she could persuade the horse-trader to let them have the pony for less money.

So busy was Kathy with her thoughts that she jumped when Daddy sang out, "See that yellow sign over there? That's the place."

They turned in the gate. The corral came into view and Kathy almost leaped from her seat. A pony stood looking over the top rail of the corral fence — a black Shetland pony. Daddy stopped beside the corral and Kathy jumped from the front seat, climbed the corral fence like a monkey and dropped on her knees beside the beautiful little pony.

"Oh you pretty little thing!" Kathy put both arms around the pony's neck. "I love you. You're going to be mine. What's your name?"

Then Kathy looked up and saw a man coming from the shack that must be his ranch house. He walked hunched over and his dirty clothes hung in rags. His face looked as though he hadn't shaved for a week. He spat out a wad of tobacco. "Git away from that there pony, you kid. She don't know ya', might give ya' a good kick and that'd give yer paw a good excuse to take me ta court."

"Oh no, sir, she likes me and we want to buy her."

"Wall ya' won't be buyin' her now. I sold her an hour ago. Told ya' this mornin'." The ugly old man turned to Daddy. "I was dead sure I had a buyer fer the pony." He glared at both of them. "Thought I was stringin' ya' didn't ya'? Well I done sold her."

The horse-trader spat another mouthful of tobacco juice

at the corral fence. "I sed, she's sold. Ya' couldn't buy her now if ya' owned all the cotton-pickin' banks in the state." He started to climb over the corral fence. "Now git outa here!"

With a last loving squeeze for the pony, Kathy scrambled over the fence and ran to Daddy. She grabbed his hand and squeezed it hard; then she began to sob aloud.

"Now Kathy, Honey, this pony isn't the only nice horse in the world. There are lots of others." Daddy stroked her hand trying to comfort her. "I should have known better than to bring you over here."

"Daddy, look at her eyes. She's smart. She could learn tricks fast and she is so shiny and beautiful . . ." Again Kathy broke out in loud sobbing.

The horse-trader cleared his throat. "I'm a gittin' another pony in on the trade for this'un . . ."

"You are?" Kathy stopped crying. "What kind of pony is it?"

"I hain't seen 'im yet, but he's s'posed to be three-year-old Welch. They'll be bringin' 'im tonight. He'll sell for a thousand dollars, too."

"We just don't have that kind of loose money." Daddy pushed back his wide-brimmed hat and scratched his head. "I do have some pure-bred cattle. Maybe we could run some kind of a trade with them."

"See that there sign a'hanging on my gate? It says HORSE-TRADER, don't it?" The man pointed a dirty finger. "If ya' got a thousand dollars worth a' pure-bred steers, maybe we kin talk business."

"On the way home, Daddy talked the horse problem over with Kathy. She sat beside him, no longer eager, but scrunched up in a huddle on the seat. She couldn't get the little black Shetland pony out of her mind. Surely there could never be so pretty a pony or such a friendly one. She wiped away the tears that ran, one by one down her nose.

The things Daddy was saying didn't make her feel one bit better.

"I don't see how we can raise a thousand dollars, even with

the steers. That amount of money is just more than the Weavers can afford for a horse."

At supper time, Kathy sat listless and quiet. She ate almost nothing. Mother laid her cool hand on Kathy's forehead and the back of her neck. "This child has a fever." she said. "We must get her to bed right away."

Daddy carried her to her room and Mother undressed her and put her in bed.

Tucked in with Seven-up in her arms, Kathy thought over all that had happened during the day. Again she felt the soft, silky coat of the little black pony lay under her hand and the pony's gentle nose against her face. Kathy cried herself to sleep.

CHAPTER 4

A Great Bargain

All night Kathy burned with fever. She drowsed between waking and sleeping. Often she heard voices and it seemed to her that Mother and Daddy talked across her bed, but she couldn't be sure because real things and imagined things got all mixed up in her mind.

She thought she heard Daddy's voice say, "I'm determined she shall have a horse of some kind . . . I'll just have to find a way."

When Kathy wakened the following day, the sun rode high in the sky. What time could it be? She wondered. How come she had slept so late? Her head didn't ache any more but it felt fuzzy and when she turned her head, her neck hurt. She wondered why she felt so weak and limp all over. She slipped out of bed and knelt to offer her morning prayer. She still knelt there by her bed when the door opened. Whoever had opened it stood there quietly until she had finished and lifted her face.

Daddy stood there with her breakfast on a pretty tray. "Well, how is my little horse-woman this morning?"

"Oh, I feel lots better, Daddy. I'm sure I'd be all well if we had a horse."

Daddy laughed. "Would you be willing to trade Lamplighter and her calf, Lollie, for a horse?"

Of all the Herefords on the ranch, Kathy liked Lamplighter

33

the best. The young cow acted so friendly. Whenever Kathy went into the cow pasture, Lamplighter followed her around smelling of her jeans and licking her arms as though she might be another calf. Now her first calf was three months old. Lollie and her mother both were beauties. Everyone on the ranch said so.

Kathy sat up in bed. Finally she spoke. "Ye-e-s." She knew how much Daddy would hate to part with Lamplighter and her calf. "She's a nice cow but she'll never do any tricks and I'm sure Lollie won't either. Cows just don't seem to be clever about doing tricks, and they can't wear saddles, of course."

Daddy laughed again. "Well, Kathy, I rode into town this morning and I thought it would be nice to get you a bunch of flowers, since you're sick; but then, just as I started into the florist's shop, a better idea came into my mind and I rode out to the horse-trader's place again. I wanted to see if he really did have another horse in, like he said he would — from that trade, you remember?"

"Did he?"

"Yes, he sure did." Daddy sat down beside Kathy. "He's got that Welsh pony he said he would get on the trade for the black Shetland pony you liked so much."

Kathy began to wriggle and squirm with excitement. "Oh Daddy, tell me more, quick."

"This pony looks fine, but I'm afraid there must be something wrong with him because the horse-trader said he was worth a thousand dollars and then he agreed to trade even for Lamplighter and her calf. I'd say those two can't possibly be worth more than $400."

Kathy felt her heart begin to race. "Did you tell him you'd make the deal?"

"Yes, I told him I thought I'd be willing to do it, but we can't finish the business until he sees Lamplighter and Lollie. He just has my word for their good points."

"When will he come to look at them?"

"This afternoon, he said."

Kathy nibbled at her breakfast. "I'd rather have a horse than a house full of flowers, even if the flowers lasted for a year."

Daddy chuckled and went out. Kathy watched from her window and saw him go out into the pasture and measure Lamplighter. She knew he must be figuring the cow's weight. She saw him write something in his notebook; then he jumped into the pickup and drove away.

Kathy crawled back into bed. She felt tired. Between fits of light sleep, Kathy opened her eyes and looked out of her window. About ten-thirty Daddy came home. A huge load of boards and poles filled the pickup. Daddy called Mack and Pete to help him and they unloaded the lumber and piled it under Kathy's window.

As the boys pulled the last of the poles from the truck, someone drove into the gate with a horse trailer. Could it be that the horse had come so soon? Kathy couldn't stay in bed a minute longer. She jumped up and stood with her nose pressed to the window pane.

The mean-looking old horse-trader got out of the car that pulled the trailer and Kathy watched Daddy lead him to the pasture gate.

For what seemed a long time to Kathy, Daddy and the old man stood looking at Lamplighter. The trader felt of the cow's legs and rump and her bag. He examined Lolly, too. Finally Kathy saw Daddy slip a halter on the cow and lead her toward the horse trailer. Lolly followed her mother. Daddy called to the boys to come and help get Lamplighter into the trailer.

Kathy shook with delight, possibly with her cold feet too, she thought, as she leaped back into bed and clutched the pillow in a fit of joy. It must be that the ugly old trader liked the cow and her calf and had made up his mind to trade for the Welsh pony. Daddy had said a Welsh pony, hadn't he? Well, a pony was a horse, any way you figured it — a horse!

Kathy could not stay in bed. Within five minutes she threw open the window and yelled at Mike and Pete who stacked

boards and poles right underneath her out-stretched hands.
"Mike, come here. Come right away, please."

Mike glanced up with a teasing look on his face and began
to walk toward the truck for another load of boards.

As he threw down the boards, Kathy called again, "Mike
come right now."

"Have to shut the gate first." Mike sauntered off as though
he had a full day to spend. Even after he'd shut the gate, he
poked along as though nothing important had happened.

"Hurry, Mike, Hurry!" Kathy waved her hands in frantic
anger. She dare not scream her fury at her brother or perhaps
he would run to the barn or get away beyond the sound of her
voice. "Mike, Mike, Mike!"

Mike came and stood beneath the window. "Kathy, you
shut that window right now. You'll catch pneumonia."

"What did Daddy say, Mike? Did he get the horse?"
Kathy's voice sounded like a wail. "Tell me, Mike."

"Shut that window, Kathy." Mike tried to reach high
enough to pull the window shut himself. "Daddy says he's
getting a Welsh pony, the one he went over to look at this
morning."

Kathy closed the window and crawled back into bed. Her
head whirled. Her feet felt as though they would never get
warm again. She still felt angry at Mike for his teasing, but
most of all she felt eaten up with wild wishing. What a day to
be sick! It's like being dead on the day when someone gives
you the whole world for a present, she thought.

She knew now that the boards and posts were going to be
used to build a corral. The boys had begun digging holes for
the posts. Daddy must really expect the horse or he wouldn't
have set the boys to building the corral.

Kathy turned on her transistor radio and brought Seven-up
from the closet shelf and cuddled under the covers again.
"Seven-up," she told the battered felt horse in her arms. "Maybe we'll have a brother for you this very day. Maybe we'd
better call him Root-Beer. That would make you twins, or

something close, anyway."

Kathy fell into a quiet sleep and some time later she wakened with a start. She heard Daddy's voice below her window. The trader must have let him off at the gate. He had left Lamplighter at the horse-trader's house, so the deal must be certain.

All alone under her covers, she squealed again and again — squeals of pure joy.

She jumped out of bed again and cracked the window six inches. "Daddy, Daddy."

He waved to her, bounded into the house while Kathy slammed the window shut and ran to meet him. She threw herself into his arms. "Did you get the horse, Daddy? Did you?"

"Yes, Honey, I made the trade, and a real bargain it is — an even trade for Lamplighter and Lolly. The pony is a beauty. You will love him."

Kathy rested in Daddy's arms and let the waves of happiness wash over her. She didn't feel a bit sick any more, just weak with joy. "Tell me about the pony, Daddy."

"Of course you already know that he's a Welsh pony . . ."

"A pony is really a horse, isn't it?"

"A pony is a horse — a small horse, just right for you."

"What color is he?"

"Chestnut, I'd say. Yes, I'm sure anyone would call him chestnut."

"Why didn't you bring him right now?"

Daddy looked out the window. "Well, I didn't want to bring him until this corral is ready. The trader says he'll bring him this afternoon. The boys should have it finished by then."

Kathy sprang from Daddy's arms and raced through the house shouting the news like a town crier. She called all the boys within hearing distance. Everyone cheered and the boys stomped their feet, whistled, and slapped each other on the shoulders.

After lunch, Kathy settled down to watch the road and the

gate. She grumbled about having to stay in bed, but Mother reminded her that she should be thankful that her window faced the side of the house where the driveway came in and where the boys worked at building the corral.

Kathy expected every truck that passed the house to turn in. When no truck came, she felt so disappointed she almost cried.

Finally, in the early afternoon, a truck did turn in and Kathy didn't even stop to take a close look at it. "He's here! He's here!" she shouted and ran clapping and shouting through the house.

Tim grabbed her shoulder. "Kathy you're crazy! Can't you see that there's hay in that truck? It isn't a horse at all."

"Young lady, if you don't calm down and say in bed, you'll be sick again and won't be able to enjoy your horse when he does come." Mother led Kathy back to bed.

Kathy propped her pillows so she could watch the gate. She saw the hay truck leave and another truck turned in. Surely this must be the horse-trader bringing the pony, but no. This truck came from the feed store in town and unloaded some bags of grain or ground feed, or something of that sort. Must be feed for the pony.

She raised up in bed and called in a loud voice, "Timmie, come here."

Timmie yelled back from the living room. "What do you want now?"

"Go see what's going on out there. Trucks keep bringing boards and poles and hay and bags of feed, but no horse."

"Oh Kathy," Timmie came into her room still holding his book. "Don't be so silly. Can't you see that the boys are hurrying to finish the corral? Looks as though you'd know they expect that horse to come today."

Kathy had to content herself with opening her window at intervals and urging the boys on. "Hurry up and get that corral done or the horse will be here before you're ready," or "I'll ask Mother to make you fellows a nice treat if you do a good quick job."

Daddy went out to help the boys, but he had barely picked up a board when a car, pulling a horse trailer, turned in the gate.

"Here he comes at last!" She held Seven-up close to the window. "Here comes Root-beer."

The rig drew up beside the nearly finished corral. Kathy could see a horse's tail switching against the slats of the trailer. She began to dance with delight. Then the driver got down from the car and she knew him at once — not the old horse trader, but the church deacon who lived down the road a couple miles. She knew that the horse in the trailer belonged to the deacon's brother. He sometimes borrowed it.

Disappointed again, Kathy turned to Seven-up. "It isn't our horse at all, Seven-up. Looks as though we are never going to get our horse."

Kathy looked at her wrist-watch, four o'clock. Now Daddy and the deacon came toward the house. A minute later they knocked at her door.

"Come in."

"I'm sorry you're sick," the deacon said as he came into the room. "Looks as though you're going to have a horse for a close neighbor." He pointed down below the window where the boys rushed about with their hammers and nails making a big stir of noise.

Daddy stood beside the deacon and he looked down too. Kathy saw a frown cross his face. He flung open the window.

Mike shouted up at him. "Corral's all done. Everything's ready. Where's that horse?"

"Everything isn't ready," Daddy snapped back. "How do you intend to get a horse into that corral without a gate?"

Kathy watched the boys' faces. Surprise flickered over them and then embarrassment, followed by disgust. Daddy and the deacon began to laugh.

"Rip the boards away from that last post and I'll come down and show you fellows how to make a gate." Daddy and the deacon left.

Kathy watched while the deacon helped Daddy make a proper gate in the corral. The boys stood around looking foolish. Good enough for that Mike, Kathy thought, serves him right for teasing me.

Night darkened the room before Kathy heard Daddy's footsteps outside her door.

He opened the door and held up his hand as though to protect himself from a blow.

Nothing could hold back Kathy's question. "Where is that horse, Daddy?"

"I don't know, Honey. I can't understand why the trader hasn't brought him. He promised to have him here this afternoon and it's night already."

"You know what I think?" Kathy's voice trembled. "I think he's a cheater. I don't think he's going to bring that horse at all. He's probably taken Lamplighter and Lolly off somewhere to trade them for some other animal."

"Don't worry so much, Kathy," Daddy said. "He does a lot of business there at his place. He may have been delayed by someone coming to look at his horses."

"No, Daddy." Kathy began to sniffle. "I know he's a crook. If you just look at his eyes, you can see that he isn't honest. We should never have trusted him."

When at last Kathy worried herself to sleep, she dreamed a frightful dream. She saw a whole herd of chestnut horses and at their head rode the ugly-faced horse trader. Kathy reached out to grab one of the horses by the mane, but couldn't get hold of it. The whole herd thundered off into a draw in the hills.

CHAPTER 5

A Welsh Pony

The rattle of horses' hoofs still rang in Kathy's dreaming mind and in her ears. She wakened slowly and saw moonlight reflected from the drifted snow in the ranch yard. Something really did rattle. She could hear it. Someone shook the window and thumped on the pane with soft thuds.

Kathy leaped out of bed and threw open the sash. A nose poked in the open window. Two nostrils blew streams of fog into the room. A wide whiskered mouth with twitching lips opened and a whinny came out. Kathy screamed and opened the window wider.

"My horse! My horse!" Her shouts tore through the ranch house.

"A brown, white-tasseled head followed the nose into the window. Kathy tried to say something, but words would not come out. She laid her face against the horse's cold furry cheek and felt the warmth of him rising through the fur.

Her bedroom door opened. Daddy, Mother and a dozen of the ranch boys crowded into the room. They laughed to see the pony's head in the window. The pony looked at them out of calm eyes and shook his white tassel at them.

Mother grabbed Kathy's robe and draped it around her like a manikin in a show window.

Kathy reached up and caressed the pony's mane. "Look, everyone," her voice had come back. "Look at my beautiful

41

horse. My Daddy got him for me." She threw both arms around the pony's neck. "And you are all mine, Root-beer."

"His name is Pom Pom," Daddy said. "Pom Pom means an ornamental ball or tassel. See, his white tassel is a pom pom."

Kathy thought for a moment. "I guess Root-beer isn't a good name for a real beautiful live horse. Calling him Root-beer would be like stepping on a Bible, or playing yo-yo in church."

"Pom Pom just fits him, such a perky name." Tim reached out to touch Pom Pom's tassel. "Reminds me of a parade. I'm sure your other horses will understand."

"What time is it, Mother?" Kathy asked.

"A little after six, time to get up and start breakfast."

"What time did the trader bring Pom Pom?"

"About midnight," Daddy told her. "Said he'd been making a trade for a couple fillies and couldn't get away any sooner."

Now all the other ranch boys came hurrying into Kathy's room, eager to see Kathy with her new horse. The first glow of dawn reddened the eastern sky, and in the growing light, the horse shone like a figure touched with gold. Gently Daddy pushed his head back outside and closed the window.

Mike rushed out yelling that he would take the first ride on Pom Pom.

"No, no," Kathy could hardly contain her excitement. "No he's my horse. I want to ride him first. Oh Daddy let me ride him first." She began to peel off her robe and darted toward the clothes closet. "I'm going to ride Pom Pom, my very own horse. No one else has the right to ride him first."

Mother stopped her. "No, Kathy, you are not well enough to go out in this cold wind. You are getting better but we can't take chances on your getting chilled and getting worse again."

Kathy hung to the closet door knob. "No, no. I feel just fine. Put your hand on my head. I haven't even a tiny bit of fever. I have to go, Mother, don't you see? I just have to ride my own horse."

A nose poked in the open window.

Mother loosened her hand from the door knob. "No, Kathy, not today." She sat Kathy down on the edge of her bed.

Kathy looked out the window and watched one boy and then another, and another, leap on Pom Pom's back and gallop around the yard. And Daddy stood there at the window laughing at the boys' crazy antics.

Kathy reached for Daddy's hand and held it against her face. How could she make Daddy understand how unfair it was for all those boys to play with her horse when she had to be shut up in her room?

"I do feel perfectly well, Daddy. Getting Pom Pom is better medicine than all the pills and cough medicine in the world."

Daddy sat down on the bed and took Kathy in his arms. "I'm sure you are better, but we can't take any chances on you. Remember we have no other little girl." He rocked her back and forth for a little while. "I know how you feel about the boys riding your pony first, but you can afford to be generous. The pony is yours, remember. And who got the wonderful good morning greeting from Pom Pom first thing?"

"I did, I did." Kathy began to laugh. "I am sorry, Daddy, for acting selfish. All the boys together haven't so much to be thankful for as I have."

"That's my good girl." Daddy tucked her into bed, arranging the pillows so Kathy could watch Pom Pom.

"Daddy, can Pom Pom do any tricks yet?"

"Not yet, I'm afraid. The trader offered to teach him tricks for $50 apiece. We can't pay him that kind of money, so I'm going to teach him myself. I do hope he has sense enough to learn."

Not for a second had Kathy taken her eyes from the pony outside her window. "What a beautiful shape he has. He is as graceful as that white horse on the cover of my horse scrapbook."

"We call a horse's shape his confirmation. Pom Pom has an excellent confirmation."

Kathy's eyes still followed the horse as though she feared

that if she looked away for an instant, he would vanish and she would wake up and find it all a dream. "What color did you say he is, Daddy?"

Daddy studied the pony for a minute. "I said he was chestnut, didn't I? Well, I said right. He's chestnut — with a white mane and tassle."

Mother came in from the kitchen. "Breakfast is ready. Do you want to wrap up and come to the table, Kathy, or shall I bring you a tray?"

"I'm not hungry." Kathy didn't turn her head from the window. "I just want to stay here and watch Pom Pom. Daddy, please tell the boys to feed him."

"No, we mustn't feed him yet," Daddy said. "I want to start teaching him his first trick, right after breakfast. He will learn quicker if he is hungry."

"What trick are you going to teach him first?"

"I'm going to try to teach him to play 'dead'."

Kathy clapped her hands. "Hurry, Daddy, hurry and eat. I can't wait to see you teach Pom Pom his first trick."

As soon as everyone had gone to the kitchen and she could hear the sounds of breakfast and the boys' table chatter she slipped out of bed, went to her dresser and combed her hair into a ponytail. She shook her head and the ponytail switched and lashed about her face just like Pom Pom's. She held the curly end of it up to the window — about the same color, too — chestnut.

She heard Daddy's voice outside. He stood just inside the corral gate with his arm stretched out toward the pony. He held half an apple in his hand. Pom Pom sniffed and came toward the apple. Daddy slipped the bridle over his head.

"Play dead, old Boy, play dead."

Kathy saw Daddy lift Pom Pom's left front foot and pull his body sharply to the right as he pushed the pony's whole body back. The surprised pony went down flat on the soft snow. Daddy held out a chunk of apple and the pony began to gobble it down. Pom Pom got to his feet and shook himself.

"Give him more apple," Kathy shouted from the window. "He's surprised and frightened. He doesn't know you yet."

Again Daddy tried to force Pom Pom down. He resisted. Finally the pony went down on his front knees and then jumped up again. "I'm beginning to think he's either stupid or stubborn, or both. He wants all apple and no trick."

"Be patient with him, Daddy, you've only been trying such a little while. See how he watches you with his big eyes? A stupid horse just couldn't have eyes like that." Kathy wished, oh, how she wished, that she could be out there helping Daddy. She just knew that Pom Pom would do what she told him because she loved him so much.

"Hit his front legs gently first and then his back legs. I'm sure he'll get the idea."

Kathy watched Daddy carry out her suggestion. Pom Pom went down all right, but shot right back up again as though he had sat on a cactus.

Daddy laughed and wiped the sweat from his face. "Well, it looks as though we can get him down, but we can't get him 'dead'."

"Try it again, Daddy," Kathy shouted. "When he's down, give him more apple."

Daddy ran around to the kitchen and came back with more apples. He put one in his shirt pocket and split the other. He tripped Pom Pom to the ground with the command, "Dead, Pom, dead!" Then he offered him a chunk of apple. Pom Pom munched the apple, laid his head on the ground and closed his eyes.

Kathy clapped her hands. "He did it right, Daddy. He did it! I told you he's a smart horse." She glanced at her watch. "It has taken you fifteen minutes. That's a fast way to make $50."

Daddy pushed back his cowboy hat and puffed a little. "At union wages that's $200 an hour. He's a fine horse, Kathy, a fine horse. Now you shut that window or you'll surely take more cold."

"Let me pet him just a little bit, first." Kathy leaned out of the window.

Daddy took off the pony's halter and he ran to Kathy. He nudged her cheek and nickered softly.

"He knows who his real trainer is." Kathy put both arms around the pony's neck and hugged him tight. "He knows who he belongs to."

Daddy drew Pom Pom away. "Now shut that window, Kathy. Shut it this minute."

All morning Kathy watched Pom Pom. Every minute she felt she couldn't love him more, but the next minute she knew that her heart had gotten a little bigger and she could love him more. Mixed with happiness over the beloved pony, worrying thoughts began to trouble Kathy. She kept thinking about what Daddy had said when the old horse trader made the even trade for Lamplight and her calf. Surely that old weasel of a trader knew that the Hereford cow and her calf could not be worth more than $400 at the outside. Could it be that Pom Pom had been stolen? Had the trader been trying to get rid of the pony fast?

Kathy called Mike to her room. "Mike, do you think my pony might have been stolen? Why would anyone let such a beautiful horse go for such a low price?"

Mike drew his face into a sad and doleful look. "Here in this neighborhood, a cheap horse often means a stolen horse." Mike heaved a deep sigh. "If he's really stolen, I suppose the sheriff will be around to pick him up."

Kathy felt a sob choke up her throat. "Pom Pom belongs to us now. No one can claim him. We bought him and paid for him."

"Then I guess it's all settled." Mike grinned in a grim sort of way. "I'll let you argue with the sheriff when he comes."

Now Kathy began to worry more than ever. Could the sheriff really come and take the pony? Would the horse trader find out what a bad bargain he'd made and come for Pom Pom?

The days went by and Kathy had no more fever or cough.

Mother let her go outside for a while every day. She watched
Daddy teach Pom Pom new tricks and every day he practiced
all the old ones so Pom Pom wouldn't forget any of them.
Everyone at the ranch knew now that Pom Pom had more
brains than most horses and also a better memory. Once he
had mastered a trick, he never forgot it.

He learned to count by pawing his left front foot the correct
number of times. He learned to kiss people and to answer
questions by nodding his head, "yes" or shaking his head, "no".
He learned to whisper things to Daddy. No question about it
any more, Pom Pom promised to be a clever trick horse. Kathy
felt sure there had never been a better one anywhere.

Then, one afternoon, a car came into the drive pulling a
horse trailer. All Kathy's worries leaped up in her mind like
terrifying monsters. Who could be coming with a horse trailer? It must be the sheriff or perhaps the horse trader. Kathy
ran to her bedroom, threw herself on her bed and buried her
face in her pillow. She knew that she could not really fight
the sheriff or even the horse trader.

CHAPTER 6

Root-beer

Kathy ran to the kitchen where she knew Daddy and the boys must be eating supper. She burst in, screaming, "Oh, Daddy, the horse trader has come to take Pom Pom away."

Daddy pushed back his chair and hurried out. Kathy grabbed her heavy jacket and followed. Mother didn't stop her. The boys all trouped out, too. That mean old wicked horse trader couldn't have Pom Pom back, no sir-ee, he just couldn't. Kathy decided that she would fight him with her own fists if he tried to lay hands on that pony.

As they rounded the corner of the house, they almost ran into a rancher whom Kathy had never seen before.

"Well, stranger," Daddy thrust out his hand and greeted the man like an old friend. "Haven't seen you around for a month of Tuesdays. How've you been?"

"Fine, Buck, fine." The strange man still stood with his cowboy hat in his hand. He looked at Kathy.

"My daughter, Kathy, Mr. Avery." Daddy took Kathy's hand. "This is the man who owns Shore Acres Ranch."

Kathy felt so relieved, she could hardly speak, but she managed to smile and remark, "How do you do? You have nice horses at your ranch."

"Thank you, little lady, I've got one customer that ain't so good." The rancher turned to Daddy. "Buck, I've got a pony

that ain't no use to me at all. Every time anyone gets on his back, he lies down flat. I've been aimin' to send him over to the dog-food factory and then I thought of you and your boys over here. I just wondered if you might be able to do something for him."

"How much do you want for him?" Daddy asked.

"I don't want a cent — just want to get him off my hands."

Daddy looked surprised. "All right, sure, we'll take him. Did you bring him along?"

"Yeah, sure, right out there in that trailer."

Daddy walked over to the trailer. Kathy still hung to his hand. In the trailer, a fine-looking buckskin pony nickered and tossed his head.

"Why he's a beauty." Kathy reached over to pat the pony.

Daddy examined the buckskin. "He surely is a fine-looking animal, Mr. Avery . . ."

Mr. Avery interrupted Daddy. "I say, 'handsome is as handsome does'." The rancher jumped into his car and slowly drew the trailer to the old corral by the barn. He helped Daddy unload the buckskin and then drove away in a big hurry as though he was afraid the buckskin might jump over the corral fence and climb back into the trailer again. Kathy heard the car and empty trailer rattle out of the front gate.

Daddy stood patting the new pony. "He's gentle and friendly and his eyes look intelligent." He combed his fingers through the pony's mane.

"How old do you think he is?" Chuck stroked the pony's glossy shoulder.

Daddy opened the pony's mouth and looked at his teeth. "I'd say he's a two-year-old. If we can just cure him of his bad habit he will make a wonderful riding horse for you boys. He is really a valuable animal."

"Do you know what his colors make me think of?" Kathy asked. "Root-beer. Remember I promised Seven-up that he'd have a brother some time."

By this time all the boys had gathered around the corral

Pom Pom has learned to play dead.

and began to make remarks about the new pony, while he walked around the inside of the fence smelling of their hands and faces, getting a pat here and a pet word there.

"I think Root-beer is a fine name for him," Timmie said, and all the other boys agreed.

"I wonder why he always lies down whenever anyone gets on his back." Daddy stood scratching his head while he watched the pony make friends with the boys.

"Let's see if he really does lie down like the rancher said." Kathy put her foot in Daddy's hand and lunged onto the pony's back. He slumped to the ground like an empty potato sack.

Kathy spanked his flank. "Come on, get up, Root-beer. Let's go." But Root-beer stretched limp on the ground.

"Can you beat that?" Daddy stood looking at the fallen horse. Now what do you suppose makes an intelligent horse like he is behave as though he didn't have any sense at all?"

"Maybe he can't resist the pull of gravity." Tim made as though he would topple over on the prostrate pony.

"I think he's lazy." Kathy kicked Root-beer a little with the toe of her pointed boot.

Daddy still looked down at the pony. "He certainly is a rebellious fellow. We may not be able to do a thing with him. You fellows work on it. I've got to get back to the shop."

Kathy got off Root-beer's back and the pony heaved himself to his feet at once.

"Let me on him." Tim leaped on the buckskin's back. "Maybe he's just a woman hater." Root-beer collapsed under Tim just as he had done with Kathy a moment before.

Kathy laughed, "Guess he doesn't like men either."

Tim picked himself up and shook his head. "It's all the same to him. Any weight on his back just mashes him down to the ground."

For a few minutes several of the boys stood around making suggestions and joking remarks, then they all left but Kathy and Tim.

"Let's put a big box under his stomach," said Tim. "Then he can't lie down."

"Then he couldn't walk either, Silly."

"While he isn't looking at you, you can slip the box out and then maybe we can get him going."

"Where will you get a big box like that?" Kathy asked.

"I guess saw horses would do if they stood tall enough."

"Those aren't good ideas at all," Kathy said. "I'm just going to have to figure it out. Come on. Let's go and ride Pom Pom. He won't lie down when we get on his back."

Kathy and Tim took turns riding Pom Pom. Then they rode together. Daddy called them. "Bring that pony to me. I need to give him some more lessons."

Kathy reined the pony in at the corral gate where Daddy waited with an apple in his hand. "Are you going to see if he remembers how to play dead?"

"Yes." Daddy took the horse. "He did pretty well this morning. I want to see how good his memory is."

No one was surprised to see Pom Pom do the 'play dead' trick as well as he had that morning.

"What trick will you teach him next?" Tim asked.

"I'm going to teach him to count by pawing with his left foot the correct number of times. You know, to tell how old he is and how old you children are. He must learn his numbers just like any other school-boy."

Daddy looked at Kathy "How did you get on with Root-beer?"

"Didn't get on at all, Daddy. Root-beer isn't smart like Pom Pom. I think he's plain stupid — a pony idiot, maybe."

Tim looked toward the barn, then began yelling like an Apache. "Look, everyone, look!"

Root-beer had just pushed the corral gate open. Before any of them could recover from their surprise, the pony walked out and began grazing on the edge of the lawn.

Daddy grabbed up the halter and ran toward the pony who lifted his head but paid no other attention. Daddy circled

around him but the buckskin went on grazing and did not try
to move away. They led him back to the corral where Daddy
examined the gate. "He didn't break it, the lock's been nudged
open. Takes a pretty smart horse to pull a trick like that."

"Maybe he's got more sense than we thought." Kathy patted Root-beer's slick coat. "Maybe we can teach him something after all."

"I surely hope so. He's smart, but a real rascal." Daddy
looked thoughtful. "It could be that when he first felt someone get on his back, he got scared or hurt. You know, perhaps
a big, fat, heavy man tried to ride him and maybe treated
him mean. Perhaps the only way he could protect himself
was to lie down."

Kathy continued to pat Root-beer. "I guess it's harder to
unlearn a horse some bad habit, than it is to teach him right
in the first place."

"You are a hundred percent correct, Kathy. The same is
true of boys and girls." Daddy turned away and went back
to Pom Pom and his tricks.

"No, I guess Root-beer isn't stupid, but he is cunning and
as stubborn as a mule." Tim said.

Then they heard Daddy calling from half way across the
lawn. "You youngsters will have to figure some way to break
that pony of his bad habit, or we'll have to let the dog-food
factory have him for sure. We can't afford to feed a no-good
horse."

Kathy and Tim looked at each other for a minute. Then
Kathy pulled Tim close and whispered. "We've just got to
do something. Seems as though I just couldn't bear to have
a pretty pony like Root-beer ground up into dog-food, could
you?"

"Look at him," Tim cried. "See how he moves his big eyes
to look at you and then at me. Looks as though he almost
knew what we're talking about."

"Well, I sure hope he does, because unless something per-
suades him to act differently, he's in for real trouble."

Kathy went back to Pom Pom's corral and watched Daddy teach the pony to count. Pom Pom knew several tricks now, and each trick he mastered seemed to make it easier for him to learn more. Yet, although Kathy felt so proud of her horse, a nagging worry disturbed her mind and she kept thinking of Root-beer and what Daddy had said. Maybe Root-beer wasn't really to blame for being ornery. People must have misused him and made him act naughty.

"I don't think it would be fair to send Root-beer to the dog-food factory," she told Daddy.

"You mean because bad treatment made him like he is?"

"Yes, it somehow doesn't seem right."

"Well Kathy, with ponies it's the same as with people. No matter how they come by their bad habits, unless they are able to overcome them they have to suffer the results."

Kathy made up her mind that she would make Root-beer her first care until he had broken his bad habit.

CHAPTER 7

A Show Horse

The brilliant March sunshine melted the last traces of snow and warmed the desert air. Kathy didn't even wear her sweater to the mailbox. As she skipped along, she thought to herself that spring promised to be early this year. She glanced at the pasture and saw Pom Pom and Root-beer both grazing on the pale new grass. They looked so peaceful and so graceful; she stood still to watch them and felt the wings of spring rising inside her. The world looked and felt so beautiful this morning.

She thought over the last few days. Everything had happened so fast. A week ago she had been longing for a horse —just any horse. Now the Weaver Ranch had two horses. She could hardly believe it.

Kathy wondered if she had come too early for the mail, but when she opened the box, there lay a stack of letters. The top envelope attracted her attention. The stamp had been cancelled in Walla Walla, Washington, and the name in the envelope's upper lefthand corner showed the same address. Kathy found the name interesting because it repeated itself, like Pom Pom. Walla Walla sounded like an Indian name. She wondered what it meant. Daddy had told her that Pom Pom meant a beautiful ornament. The envelope with its red and blue airmail border looked Indian, too. Kathy felt sure the letter must have something important inside.

Kathy and Murray have pulled Pom Pom from the quicksand.

She would take it to Daddy at once.

She raced up the drive and into the house. "Where's Daddy?"

"Here I am." Daddy's voice called. "I'm here at my desk."

"Look — an airmail letter from Walla Walla. What does Walla Walla mean?"

"I wondered that once myself, Kathy, so I looked it up. The name belonged to a tribe of Indians and it means 'Rushing Water'." Daddy ripped open the envelope and unfolded the letter.

When he had finished reading it, he looked up at Kathy. "This letter is from my old friend, Frank, up in Walla Walla, Washington. He's heard about our Boys' Ranch and he has a boy he'd like to send down here. He's asked me to come up to speak at the college there in Walla Walla. He wants me to tell about the ranch and take a look at the boy."

"You'll go, won't you, Daddy?" Kathy felt excitement rise in her like a flying bird and she added in a breathless voice. "You will take me with you, of course."

Daddy leaned back and laughed so hard he dropped the letter.

Kathy laid her hand on Daddy's shoulder. "We will take Pom Pom too. He's learned enough tricks so he can help you give a program."

"I don't know about taking Pom Pom, Kathy. We've only had him a short time and while he does his tricks all right here in his own corral, maybe he wouldn't perform at all in front of an audience."

"Daddy, don't you think God has arranged this Walla Walla thing to give Pom Pom a chance?"

"That, I couldn't say." Daddy ran his hands through his hair and Kathy knew he must be thinking hard.

"Let's try it, Daddy. I'm sure Pom Pom won't disappoint us."

Still Daddy hesitated, "It's such a long way to haul the pony in the horse trailer, and for just one appearance. Maybe it's foolish to think of such a thing. We'd better go and ask Mother."

Mother caught Kathy's enthusiasm. "Of course you must take the pony. He will surely perform for the people and that will be a big step forward toward his becoming a real showhorse."

"What do you think of Kathy going along?" Daddy asked.

"Well, no, I don't know about that. She's been sick so recently . . . . ."

"Oh, Mother, I'm all well. With this spring smell in the air I feel like skipping and running all the time. I just have to see Pom Pom give his first performance. I have to!"

"The boys won't like putting on your apron and doing your kitchen jobs." Mother winked at Daddy. "Perhaps I can persuade them."

"I know Timmie will do my work. I just know he will." Kathy ran to find her youngest brother.

When she found Tim and brought him back ready to swear faithfulness in all of Kathy's chores, Daddy already sat at his desk with writing paper in front of him. "I am suggesting to Frank that we would like to put on a program with a trained horse. I'm sure he will arrange it. He loves horses."

During the next few days, while they waited for an answer from Walla Walla, Daddy trained Pom Pom for longer hours and with harder tricks than he had ever tried before. When Frank called by telephone, accepted the plan and fixed a date two weeks ahead, the Weaver Ranch exploded into enthusiastic activity. Dad worked with Pom Pom every day. For each working day of the two weeks he put Pom Pom through every trick.

Kathy hovered about the corral, suffering agonies when Pom Pom failed, and bursting with joy when the pony went through his tricks without hesitation. To her the two weeks before the Walla Walla trip seemed more like two days.

The great morning dawned at last and Pom Pom seemed eager to start. He walked up into the trailer without any urging at all. Mike begged to go along on the trip. "You'll surely need a man along," he told Daddy, giving Kathy a scornful look.

"I'm sure you're right, Mike," Daddy said. "But you see we must save a seat for that new boy we expect to bring back with us."

"Does Kathy have to go?" Chuck joined in the argument. "What good will she be?"

"I'm a lot of good, Chuck Weaver," Kathy hopped into the truck. "I am a big comfort to Pom Pom and to Daddy too. He always says so." She settled herself in the narrow front seat. "Pom Pom is my horse and where he goes, I go."

Daddy laughed, stepped on the starter and they rolled out the gate and turned north.

The ride could not be called comfortable. The sun felt too hot for this time of year and much of the road seemed to be pitted with chuck-holes or broken by mean little dips that jolted both truck and trailer. A flat tire delayed them, but Daddy had a spare all prepared and soon replaced the broken tire with a good one. They reached Walla Walla on Friday afternoon.

"Well, here we are, Kathy. This is the Walla Walla College campus."

"It's beautiful, Daddy, but this truck has been like a churn and I feel like a pat of butter. I'd like to get out."

Daddy laughed, "I feel about the same way, myself. You see, they put stiff shock absorbers on trucks, but this one sure does need a new pair." They both climbed down from the truck.

"We'll get a bath now and have a good rest for a whole day. Our program isn't until tomorrow evening."

"I'm sure Pom Pom needs a rest as much as we do." Kathy went back to the trailer to look at her pet. "With several hundred miles of jerking and jolting, it's a good thing he doesn't have to give that program tonight."

By the following evening, Kathy felt so rested that she

could stand in the big auditorium and feel as though she must shout for joy. She could hardly wait for the curtain to go up on Pom Pom's first performance.

Then, as the audience trooped in, she began to twist her hands. Every seat seemed to be filled. How awful if Pom Pom should fail; but of course he wouldn't. Yet the sight of so many people — it almost frightened Kathy. What would a horse think of it?

Kathy looked across the aisle at the boy, Murray Jackson, who would go back to the ranch with them tomorrow. His hair hung in long red straggles and a million freckles spotted his face. He wore a rubber spider on his left shirt front. Did he think he could scare anyone with that fake? He looked like some strange insect himself. She tried to think what bug she had seen in the encyclopedia that reminded her of Murray. Then she saw him pick the spider off his chest and throw it at a little girl. The surprised child shuddered and sobbed.

"It's time for me to teach that Murray his first lesson in good manners," Kathy said to herself as she jumped up and stood over Murray. "Murray Jackson, pick up that spider at once and sit down in your place. You frightened that little girl and made her cry."

Murray let out a belly-laugh, but he sat down, reached for the spider and dropped it into his pants pocket.

Kathy sat down again and began to worry because the program had not yet begun. What could be wrong? Had Pom Pom given them trouble? She had just decided to go back stage to see what had delayed Daddy, when the lights went out and a man came to the microphone in the center of the stage to introduce Daddy. Then, as spotlights played on him, Daddy introduced Pom Pom and the audience applauded with a polite spatter of handclapping.

Daddy stood there with his big bright smile and spoke to Pom Pom. "Let's have a kiss, Old Boy." he said, and the pony kissed him. Everyone laughed.

Daddy talked to Pom Pom, asking him questions which

the pony answered with a nod of his head for "Yes" and a shake for "No."

Kathy began to relax. Pom Pom didn't act at all scared. With every new trick, the audience grew more interested and the clapping sounded louder and lasted longer. Pom Pom seemed to enjoy the applause and went through his tricks so gracefully that Kathy laughed herself into tears. Everyone in the hall doubled over with laughter when the pony stole Daddy's gloves and pulled the saddle blanket from his own back. When he played dead, everyone went wild, and clapping, stomping and shouting shook the building.

Kathy saw Pom Pom leave the stage and Daddy began singing a western song to close the program.

She knew now that Pom Pom had made a great success of his first appearance. She knew he had earned some money, too, but she cared nothing for that, just for Pom Pom reigning like a king up there on the high stage with all those people admiring and loving him.

When the curtain dropped, Kathy clapped louder and longer than anyone else. Even when the audience began to break up, Kathy's loud clapping still echoed through the hall.

The following morning the Weaver truck started home.

A bright Sunday morning spread clear and crisp along the highway south. Kathy, Daddy and Murray sat in the cab of the truck watching the scenery as they rolled toward the home ranch.

Kathy squeezed as close to Daddy as she could. Murray looked so dirty and sloppy and he didn't smell good either. Kathy didn't want to touch him. He wriggled a lot too. She felt that unless he quit jiggling around, she would scream. She tried to make herself small and scrunched up close to Daddy.

Then one of the tires blew out with a shattering bang.

"Oh no!" Daddy groaned. "Another tire, and I forgot to have the spare repaired in Walla Walla. I'll have to take the spare and hitch a ride to the nearest garage." He got out and began to loosen the spare tire. "Now Kathy, you and Murray stay here. Just sit in the truck and watch Pom Pom."

Daddy hailed several trucks and finally a pickup stopped. He pitched the spare tire onto the open truck-bed and jumped into the cab with the strange driver. The pickup rolled away in a cloud of dust.

Kathy looked out over the empty, semi-desert country and a feeling of deep lonesomeness pressed up in her chest. How far would Daddy have to go? Would he ever get back?

Pom Pom began to move about restlessly in his trailer. He began to kick and shake the wheels. Both children got out. Murray climbed into the trailer with the pony, petted him and talked to him. Kathy had to admit that Murray knew how to quiet a horse. He had already made friends with Pom Pom.

Murray stuck his head out of the horse trailer. "Kathy, I think this horse is thirsty."

"Throw me his empty bucket and I'll try to find some water." Kathy caught the bucket and scrambled down the steep bank hunting for water.

A little way from the road, she found a shallow, sluggish stream flowing among tall grasses and cattails. She hurried toward it and felt loose, damp sand sift into her shoes.

She filled the bucket as full as she could without a dipper and made long difficult jumps to get out of the sand and back onto the dirt path. She climbed the steep embankment and then she saw that Murray had taken Pom Pom out of the trailer and was grazing him along the roadside.

"Murray, why did you do it?" Kathy put the bucket of water down.

"Because it took you so long. Pom Pom is hungry and real thirsty. I thought you were never coming back. Did you bring any water?"

"A little." Kathy held the partly filled pail under Pom Pom's nose. He sucked it up in a couple long swallows. "See, it's only a taste for him. It's awful hard to get that water, it's so shallow and so much grass and weeds in it."

Murray looked into the empty bucket. "We'll just have to take Pom Pom down there and let him get his drink his own self. Come, show me where it is." He turned the pony toward the steep embankment.

"What if Daddy comes back while we're gone? It's been hours since he left." Kathy felt uneasy about leading the pony off the road. "We can't let him fall, Murray. He might break a leg."

Murray didn't answer, but Kathy saw that he led the pony at an angle and he reached the level ground without mishap. "Now where's that water?"

Kathy pointed out the stream and Murray allowed Pom Pom to wade in among the reeds where he drank the water eagerly.

The two children waited patiently. Pom Pom had satisfied himself and seemed to be standing there enjoying the feel of the cool water on his feet.

"Come on. Murray, we'd better get him back up the bank. He's through drinking.

"Come along, Pom Pom." Murray pulled on the halter rope, but the pony did not move.

"What's the matter with him, Murray?" A chill ran up and down Kathy's spine. He always minds real well."

Murray urged the pony with strong pulls on the rope and pleading words. Pom Pom tried to move, but he seemed glued to the bottom of the shallow stream. He began to struggle, but his struggles did not help at all.

"Kathy," Murray's voice trembled with fright. "Kathy, he's sinking in that fine sand!" His eyes bulged and he leaned forward to see this terrible thing. "It's quicksand, Kathy. Quicksand!" His voice rose to a shriek.

Kathy began to cry. "Oh Murray, he will sink clear down under." She took a step forward. She must go on to Pom Pom. She must help him.

Murray grabbed her arm and held her back. "Don't go one step farther. You will sink too."

"But what shall we do? We must do something. He will drown." She began to cry aloud.

"Don't cry, Kathy. That won't do a bit of good. Run back to the truck and see if your Dad has come back. If he hasn't, grab the rope in the trailer and bring it as fast as you can."

Kathy scrambled up the embankment, trying to stifle her sobs as she climbed. She could see nothing through her tear-blinded eyes and lost her footing and rolled to the bottom of the slope. She screamed, "Daddy! Daddy!" but no voice answered. Breathless and scratched, she got to her feet and began once more to climb.

No sign of Daddy anywhere. She climbed into the truck for the rope and found it tied fast to a ring attached to the cab. Her small fingers fought with the hard knot, but with her hands all trembly and her eyes full of tears, she could do nothing with the knot. She could not possibly get it loose in time to save Pom Pom. She began to cry again and then thought how useless crying was. She relaxed, bowed her head, and prayed.

CHAPTER 8

Murray

Kathy opened her eyes and knew that the moment
of prayer and relaxation had quieted her. Now her fingers
worked better, the knot began to loosen. Her knee knocked
against a loose bolt and she tried to pry it free. With the bolt
as a wedge, she began to loosen the inner loops of the knot.

A truck drew up alongside and Kathy heard Daddy's voice.
He called her name. She leaped from her cramped position
and stuck her hand out the door of the cab. "Here I am, Daddy. Hurry, come and help me quick!"

"What's the matter? Where's Murray? Where's Pom Pom?"
Daddy propped the spare tire against the truck's fender.

"Down there." Kathy waved wildly toward the embankment. "Pom Pom's caught in the quicksand. We have to have
this rope."

Daddy jumped into the trailer and soon had the knot un-
done. "Come, let's go. Show me the place."

At the stream, Murray stood waving his arms beckoning
them. Kathy could see that Pom Pom's belly had sunk deep
into the water.

Daddy looked about for something to throw out into the
stream to support him. A wooden fence-post lay close to the
embankment, still fastened to a strand of barbed wire. Daddy twisted the wire off and tossed the post into the water
beside Pom Pom.

He fastened the rope around Pom Pom's body just behind his front legs and told the children to pull. Balancing himself on the fence post, Daddy pulled the pony's legs, one by one, from the sucking sand. Pom Pom struggled out of his trap and leaped to solid ground. Kathy and Murray cheered.

"I think he must have touched solid bottom," Daddy said. "That quicksand seems rather shallow. If it had been deep, he would have already suffocated — a close call, kids. Teaches us to be on the lookout for quicksand, might find it anywhere in this country."

Back at the truck, the children grazed Pom Pom along the roadside while Daddy changed the tire. Then he helped them get the pony back into the trailer.

"Okay, kids, into the cab. We've got to really make tracks. We lost too much time here."

"How far are we from home?" Kathy snuggled against Daddy in the truck seat.

"Four hundred miles at least. We'll sleep in a motel tonight and hit the hi-way early in the morning."

The following morning, as the truck rolled along toward home, Kathy amused herself and Murray by telling him about Root-beer and his big problem. "We've tried and tried, but he still lies down flat whenever anyone mounts him."

Kathy saw that under Murray's tousled hair his eyes shone bright and twinkly. He seemed to take great pleasure in hearing about Root-beer.

The truck finally crossed the Nevada state line and Kathy gave a whoop of joy. When, at last, tired and dusty, they turned in the gate of the Weaver Ranch, she hit the horn to alert the whole family. They would all want to hear about Pom Pom's performance at Walla Walla.

The truck jolted to a stop. Kathy saw Mother at the Ranch house door and boys came running from every direction. Murray climbed down and Kathy slid after him.

"This is Murray." Kathy introduced the new boy to everyone.

The boys acknowledged Murray's presence with nods and smiles, but they could not wait any longer to put the big question. "How did the show go? How did Pom Pom do his tricks?"

"He was great — just great!" Kathy pressed through the boys and ran to hug Mother. Murray trotted right behind her and Kathy introduced him to Mother.

"Nice to meet you, Murray." Mother held out her hand and smiled. "Dinner's ready. Come, everyone."

Kathy looked at Murray's hands. They were positively filthy. How dared he shake hands with Mother?

"Wash up, everyone," Mother sang out in her friendly voice.

At the dinner table the gang of ranch boys gave Murray curious glances. As Kathy served the soup she set a steaming bowlful down in front of Murray. He filled his spoon and put it to his lips, then he gasped, "Ouch, it's hot!"

He puckered his lips and blew on the spoonful of soup. It spattered in every direction.

"Hey, do you furnish towels with your showers?" Peter wiped soup from his cheek.

"Have some bread to hold it down." Mike pushed the bread plate toward Murray. He grabbed a slice of the fresh bread and dunked the whole piece in his soup, then gobbled it up in great noisy slurps.

Mike began to laugh and Kathy kicked him under the table. She picked up her spoon and began to eat. Mike began to suck up his soup with disgusting noises. Peter began to eat his soup the same way.

Kathy looked at Murray who seemed to have a cold and a runny nose. She ran to the bathroom and brought him a Kleenex. Murray blew his nose with as much gusto as he had slurped his soup.

"The diesel approaches the crossing — —" Mike yanked out his handerchief and blew his nose in a thunderous burst of noise.

"Boys, boys," Mother raised her hand. "Let's not forget our manners." Kathy did not miss the sober look on Mother's face.

"We're just trying to make Murray feel at home." Chuck grinned.

Kathy saw that Murray needed another tissue, but decided he could get it for himself this time. "The Kleenex is in the bathroom," she whispered.

"I don't need no Kleenex," Murray snuffled.

"But you do, Murray . . ."

"Okay, where's the bathroom?" Murray rose from the table looking in the direction of Kathy's pointing finger. He bumped his chair and tipped it over, then stumbled over the fallen chair and fell flat on the floor. Kathy saw that he had tripped himself on his long shoelaces.

"Murray!" Kathy stooped to help him up. "You must tie your shoelaces. You're going to hurt yourself some day if you don't."

"Well-ventilated feet stimulate the brain." Mike coughed and all the boys doubled up with laughter.

Kathy saw Murray's face flush — red as his hair. She tried not to laugh as she led him to the Kleenex box.

"While you're here, might as well comb your hair." She handed him a comb and left him raking it through the tangles of his fiery hair. Kathy dashed back to the table and got in on the end of Dad's lecture about taking it easy with Murray and giving him a chance. "After all, this boy hasn't had the opportunities you fellows have had."

Murray came back with his shoelaces tied, but walking on his pants cuffs. His newly combed hair stood straight up. He looked as though he had just been badly frightened.

"So, the Leaning Tower of Pisa is carrot colored . . ."

"Mike!" Father's firm voice squelched the wave of laughter. "That will be enough. This afternoon we will have a hair-cutting session and Murray may have the first turn."

Right after lunch Kathy found Murray and insisted that

he must wash his hair. "Come on, here's the shampoo. I'll show you how."

Even Murray seemed surprised at the color of the water after the first soaping and when he had finished, his hair felt much softer and looked several shades lighter.

"Now you'd better go out in the sun and dry that hair. Daddy will be coming to cut it in an hour or so."

Kathy watched Daddy run the barber shears across the top of Murray's head until the bright red hair stood out only an inch from his head. Daddy did a fine job, even shaved all the straggly hairs on Murray's neck and around his ears.

"You look real good with a 'Butch', Murray." Kathy swept the red hair into a dustpan.

"Burr-rr-r, I feel cold, like I didn't have any clothes on." Murray looked at himself in the mirror Kathy held up for him and scowled.

Mother appeared at the door. "One of the neighbors outside to see you," she told Daddy.

Daddy unpinnd the beach towel from around Murray's neck and dusted him off, then hurried outside. Kathy followed him and Murray trailed behind them.

"Got something I want to show you." The man grinned and led Daddy over to his truck. Kathy and Murray reached the truck as soon as Daddy did. They climbed up and looked in. "Puppies, Daddy!" Kathy squealed with delight. "Aren't they the sweetest little things?" She hopped over into the truck bed. Murray tumbled in after her and the puppies, twelve of them, swarmed over them.

Kathy held up a little black pup with brown markings on his face. "Isn't he a dream?"

Murray took the puppy and held it close to his face, calling it pet names.

The neighbor man stood beside the truck talking with Daddy. "Buck, I've got these dogs I'd like to get rid of. They're too valuable to drown and I haven't time to peddle them around."

"I want this one." Murray held up the black and brown puppy. "Please let me have him, Mister Weaver. See, he knows me."

With her arms full of wriggling puppies, Kathy joined her plea with Murray's. "Let him have the puppy, Daddy. He hasn't got one thing of his own."

Daddy held up his hand. "Wait, wait, we've got to think this thing through."

Like bees drawn to honey, the boys raced from all directions and climbed into the truck. The puppies were grabbed up and fondled. A hub-bub of voices arose. "I want this one." " This one is going to be mine."

Dad jumped onto the truck and shouted for everyone to be quiet. He looked like an auctioneer ready for business. "How many of you boys would like to have one of these dogs? It will mean that you each will have to take care of your own dog and train it. No training, no dog." He paused a minute and looked down at the boys with their arms full of puppies. "Now each of you who wants a puppy and will take all responsibility for it, raise your hands."

Ten hands shot up.

"Okay, fellows, choose your dogs." Daddy jumped down and so did Kathy.

Such a lot of dogs, Kathy wasn't sure she liked the idea. What would Jet think? With two horses and Jet, they really didn't need ten more dogs, but Daddy must know best.

Murray started for the house and Kathy followed him into the kitchen. She opened the refrigerator and poured milk into a bowl. She set it on the floor and Murray sat down with his puppy beside the dish.

"The little feller's hungry." Murray stroked the soft fur. "Guess that old guy didn't feed his dogs very good."

Kathy filled three more bowls and set them outside. Nine puppies crowded round them. "Jeepers, this place has turned into a kennel — Weaver's dog heaven." Kathy tried to remind the boys that they must feed their dogs themselves. "For if you don't, Daddy will send them right back where they came from."

Jet came up and looked with surprise at the swarm of puppies. Kathy gathered him into her arms. "You are my dog, Jet. You were here first and you are best of all."

At supper Daddy announced that all the dogs would sleep on the back porch. Kathy saw a peculiar look cross Murray's face and she hung around that evening to see how he would fix up his puppy for the night. She waited until the lights had been snuffed and prayers said; then she took up her watch at one of the windows that overlooked the porch.

Just as she expected, a slight, pajama-clad figure stole silently out onto the porch, picked up a puppy and stuffed it into his pajama jacket. He disappeared into the boys' sleeping quarters. Murray!

The next few weeks turned out to be busy ones for the new dog-masters. Some of the boys neglected their puppies and Daddy took them back to the farmer, but Murray tended his pet every day and every night. As soon as the puppy grew old enough to train, he taught it to have good manners and to do tricks. Kathy always managed to be around where she could help him.

One afternoon when the children had already spent an hour playing with the puppy and training him, they started for the corral to feed Pom Pom and Root-beer.

"I hear that you take your dog to bed with you at night." Kathy said. "I'll bet Daddy doesn't know."

"Shhh! It's a secret. He's so warm and cuddly and he gets so lonesome alone. Please don't tell on me, Kathy."

"Look, Murray," Kathy screamed and grabbed the boy's shoulder. "Look! There's a snake. You almost stepped on it — looks like a rattler!"

"This here snake's no rattler." Murray picked it up. "See it's a garter snake. Look at his tail. There's no rattles on it."

Kathy backed away. "What are you going to do with it, kill it or throw it away?"

"I'm not going to do neither. I'm going to keep him for a pet. I'll make a cage for him."

"What will you feed him?"

"Frogs, toads, earthworms. We'll have lots of fun feeding him."

"Well if you're determined to keep him, you'll have to make a cage for him. Come on. There should be some old boxes in the barn loft."

Murray wrapped the snake neatly around his arm, then the two of them climbed the ladder to the barn loft. Kathy pointed to an old box with torn sheets of tarpaper piled on top. Murray picked up the corner of one sheet and quickly dropped it.

"What's the matter?" Kathy jumped back. "Another snake?"

"No, mice, a whole nest full of baby mice."

Murray held the snake out to Kathy. "Hold him while I trap these mice."

"No. I don't want to." Kathy shivered.

"Aw, come on, you're no sissie, even if you are a girl." Murray took a step toward her. "See, just take him right below the head."

Kathy reached out slowly and took the snake. She was surprised. It felt smooth and — rather nice, not slimy nor spooky at all.

Murray looked around the loft and spotted a piece of window screen. He carefully slid the piece of screen under the sheets of tar-paper and lifted it off. "Now look at the baby mice."

"They are kind of cute," Kathy admitted. "What are you going to do with them?"

"I'm going to keep them. I'll nail the screen down and make a fine nest for them."

"What'll they eat?"

Murray scratched his head, "I hadn't thought of that. Maybe I'd better feed them to the snake. He would like that."

Kathy shivered. "Here take your old snake. I don't see

anything to keep him in."

"I do." Murray grabbed up an empty mayonnaise jar. "This is perfect. We'll punch holes in the cover so he'll get enough air."

"Where will you keep all these creatures?" Kathy asked.

"Under my bed."

"Under your bed? Daddy won't like that — the boys won't either."

"If you don't tell them, they'll never find out."

Kathy helped Murray clean the jar and pierce holes in the lid. Murray put some soft grass in the bottom and gently lowered the snake into the cozy nest.

They slipped into the house and pushed both snake and mouse cages under Murray's bed. Kathy pulled down the spread so no one could see them. Then they ran out to scour the ranch for snake food.

CHAPTER 9

Last Chance for Two

The weeks passed quickly and spring came to the Weavers' Boys' Ranch. One April morning, Kathy, wedged in between Chuck and Tim, rode with Daddy and Mother to the shopping center in town.

Mother took a deep breath of the sweet fresh air. "Oh, that smells so good. You know the boys' room doesn't smell good at all. It seems to flavor the whole house."

"It smells like a zoo, Mother," Chuck spoke up. "It has ever since Murray started keeping all his animals under his bed."

"He seems determined to sleep with his dog," Daddy said. "Animals never smell good when they're penned up." He shook his head. "I'm afraid Murray is no perfumed blossom himself."

"Yeah, Dad, he really stinks worse'n his animals." Chuck said. "And he's such a stupid guy. The other day he said in class that Chicago is the capital of California."

Kathy felt provoked at Chuck. "Oh yeah, you guys are all so smart. Well just remember that Murray is the only boy who took a puppy and really looked after it and trained it." Kathy stuck a chew of gum in her mouth and offered a stick to Mother.

Mother took the gum. "Thank you, Kathy. What you say is true and that's a good point for Murray, but he really is very careless. When I made him polish his shoes for church,

"Here, stand on my hand."

he did a real good job right on his bed. The spread is smeared all over with shoe-polish."

Dad slowed the car at a red light and pulled to a stop. He rested his hands on the steering wheel and turned to Mother. "That kid is a meddler, too. Yesterday I caught him trying to teach Pom Pom to count. Afterward, when I tried to practice with Pom Pom, he seemed confused. Murray must have given different signals. We simply can't have that!"

"You're right," Mother said. "We can't have Pom Pom spoiled."

"But Murray is a good salesman." Tim reached his hand for some gum. "You know those envelopes you had us sell last week? Well, Daddy, he sold the most. He was dirty, too, the only one of us boys that wasn't spanking clean."

Mother thought for a moment. "Yes, there are good things about Murray, but being kind to animals and being a good salesman will not freshen the air in that bedroom. It isn't fair for the other boys to be forced to put up with his smells. I'll just have to find another place for Murray and his animals."

The light changed and Dad stepped on the gas. "I think we have no choice but to let Murray go back to Walla Walla. He is careless and dirty and I will not have Pom Pom spoiled. Yes, that's settled. Murray will have to go."

Kathy gasped, but she did not speak. She sat all the rest of the way into town in complete silence. She knew that Daddy could not be argued with in this mood, but she thought fast and hard.

She and Chuck came out of the super-market with big sacks of groceries. She set hers carefully in the ranch wagon, then turned to find Tim behind her. His sack had a big tear in the bottom and when they set it down it ripped open and cans of food, bars of soap and boxes of matches rolled in every direction. Kathy helped Tim pick them up and put them in an empty carton. Then they sat in the car and waited for Daddy and Mother to come out of the Five-and-Ten.

"I just feel awful about Murray having to leave," Kathy

said.

"Me too," Tim opened a new package of gum. "I don't mind him being dirty so much, since he's so kind to animals."

"Kathy, you are the one who begged and whined for a show horse until you got one." Chuck sucked on a life-saver. "If Dad lets Murray go on mixing Pom Pom up about his tricks, then all your dreams about a show-horse will go a glimmering."

"Daddy could forbid him to go near Pom Pom," Kathy said. "He wouldn't dare to disobey Daddy."

"Humph! Like telling a bee to lay off the honey." Chuck laughed.

"Since he loves horses so much, why can't he mess around with Root-beer?" Kathy racked her brain to think of some way to solve Murray's problem. "I'm sure Murray would go for that."

"Root-beer's no attraction, Kathy." Tim turned up his nose. "Root-beer still flattens out like a soggy biscuit when anyone tries to ride him."

Kathy paid no attention to the boys' discouraging comments. She smiled again and felt a lot better. Deep down some place inside her she knew that she had hit on the right answer. Turn Root-beer over to Murray to train and teach just like Daddy worked with Pom Pom.

On the way home Kathy suggested her plan about Root-beer.

Daddy thought for quite a long time. "That really isn't a bad idea, Kathy, not bad at all. Root-beer is going to turn over a new leaf too or he goes to the dog-food factory. Murray and that buckskin are in the same fix, they've got to trim up or something real bad is going to happen to them." Daddy drove for a mile or two still thinking. Kathy waited. "You know, folks, I'm inclined to give both Murray and Root-beer one more chance. Of course, if they don't improve they will have to go."

He turned to Mother. "Don't you think it's possible that

they might cure each other?"

"I'm certainly willing to give them another chance. Let's hope and pray that it works."

Kathy and Tim clasped their hands together and shook them with glad relief. Kathy could hardly wait to get home.

Daddy seemed to read her mind. "Now you let me put this proposition to Murray. I intend to really impress it on his mind that this is the last chance he's going to get."

Back at the ranch, Kathy listened while Daddy gave Murray the worst scolding he'd ever given any of the ranch boys. She saw Murray's face turn from pale fright to flushed pleasure when Daddy told him, "so I am giving Root-beer into your special charge. You are to be his master just as I am Pom Pom's master. I want you to break him of his bad habit and make him into a good reliable horse. I think you can do it."

The wind fluttered Kathy's blue dress as she raced with Murray to the corral. There Murray caught Root-beer and put the halter on him.

"Climb on his back, Kathy. No use saddling him until we break him of this silly idea."

Kathy reached up. "He's taller than Pom Pom. I can't get up without stirrups."

"Here, stand on my hand." Murray helped her to Root-beer's back.

Then the buckskin's legs began to go down and Kathy slid backward. "Feels like coasting down a hair-slide on your tummy."

"Hold on Kathy, I'll try to heist him up. Murray began to tickle Root-beer's hind legs with a foxtail, but the pony kept on going down till he lay flat on the ground.

Kathy looked over toward the barn and saw Mike doubled over in side-splitting laughter. "Tie his legs together," Mike hollered. "Let him sit on the ground for twelve hours, or give him a good licking and he'll be ready to stand up."

Murray shook his head. "No. Patience is the only cure for this kind of disease."

Kathy looked at him. "That's another way of saying 'Love will win' isn't it?"

"Yeah, I s'pose so. And it's going to take a lot of both love and patience to cure Root-beer, I'll bet."

"Look, Murray, shouldn't we reward Root-beer with bits of apple and lumps of sugar — you know — the way Daddy does with Pom Pom?"

"He ain't done one thing to be rewarded for yet."

"Maybe sugar and apples would get him into the right mood, " Kathy said. "I'll go get some."

She came back in a minute with sugar cubes in her jeans pocket and an apple in her hand. She had changed her clothes while she was in the house.

Root-beer had gotten to his feet again and he stood there looking at Murray and Kathy with such an innocent expression on his face that they both had to laugh.

"Bite out a piece of this apple, Murray, and when I get on his back this time, give it to him."

"I can't feed him apples and help you onto his back at the same time." Murray bit into the apple.

"I'll go and fetch the old stepladder." Kathy ran off to the house, grabbed up the ladder and dragged it to Root-beer's side. She spread the ladder's legs, perched on top of it and prepared to spring onto the pony's back at exactly the right instant.

"Okay, Murray, feed him the sugar cube while I get on. Then give him the bit of apple."

Root-beer seemed to relish the sugar cube and stood still for a minute, but after he had swallowed the peace offerings, his front legs began to wilt, then his hind legs folded and he went down in a disgusting heap.

Mike watching from the hedge where he worked at his pruning job, roared with laughter again. He fetched an armload of pyracantha twigs and branches intending to dump it on the rubbish heap back of the barn. "Put this pile of thornbrush under him. I'll warrant he'll think twice before he melts

again."

Neither Kathy nor Murray paid any attention to Mike's teasing, but stood staring at the horse in silence. Kathy knew Murray had got his brains to working at last. He did have brains, she knew.

"Kathy, let's pretend he's just a young colt being broken for the first time. Go get a blanket from the house . . . Fetch your biggest doll, too. I have an idea."

She ran to her room, pulled a blanket from her bed and picked up a life-sized baby-doll that sprawled on her closet floor.

On her rush out the door, she met Mike. "Well, look at Poco-haunt-us, with her papoose, out to conquer Thunderbolt!"

"Mike, you are the world's biggest nuisance. Can't you tend to your own business and let us tend to ours?" She hurried back to Root-beer and Murray.

"Here's the blanket and the doll." She thrust them at Murray. "Now what are you going to do?"

"We'll throw the blanket over his back and make him walk for quite a while with just the blanket." Murray leaned the doll against the corral fence and gently spread the folded blanket on the buckskin's back. He grabbed the halter rope and led him into a brisk trot.

He came back breathless to Kathy. "After he's used — to the weight — of the blanket — we'll add the doll."

"You don't think he'll lie down when we put the doll on him?" Kathy ran along beside Murray as he started around the corral the second time with Root-beer.

"The doll isn't very heavy. I think he'll take it all right. The idea is to add weight little by little."

The corral seemed too small for racing the horse around as they wished, so Kathy and Murray led Root-beer out to the main hi-way where they walked and trotted him for more than a mile. Finally Root-beer slowed down and nothing could persuade him to go faster. But when they turned his nose toward home, he broke into a fast trot and Murray had

"Put this pile of thornbrush under him. I'll warrant he'll think twice before he melts again."

trouble holding him back.

The blanket began to slide off and Kathy ran close beside the pony and pulled it straight. Back at the ranch she opened the corral gate. She decided they must have been gone about an hour.

"I think it's time to straddle that doll on his back now," Murray said.

"I'll bring her." Kathy ran to get the doll. She took it to the top of the stepladder. "Now bring him alongside, Murray, and hold your breath. If he goes down when we sit the doll on him, all our work today is wasted."

"Maybe not, Kathy. At least we know he can bear the weight of a blanket, that's something." Murray brought Root-beer into position so Kathy could set the doll on his back. "Put it on easy — easy."

"Easy as I can," Kathy whispered the words as she reached over to set the doll, oh so lightly on the buckskin's back. She didn't touch the horse, then waited a breathless moment.

Slowly Root-beer's front legs went down, then his hind legs and he lay in a collapsed heap at their feet. Kathy felt like crying and Murray looked as though he might cry too if he were a girl.

Finally Murray spoke. "You know what we're going to do, Kathy? We are going to let Root-beer alone the rest of this day, then tomorrow we'll go through that blanket business again. We'll make him tote blanket for three days straight."

Kathy couldn't help but admire Murray's patience. "I guess we got a little too eager," she said. "It'd be a little much to expect Root-beer to reform in just one day, wouldn't it?"

"Yes, it would."

Murray kept his word. Root-beer got used to carrying the blanket. Then Murray added another blanket and the buckskin accepted the added load. A week later he decided that the time had come to try the doll.

This time Kathy felt more confident. "I'm almost sure he'll take the doll, Murray," she said as she climbed the step ladder

with the doll in her arms. Again Murray backed Root-beer
into position. Again Kathy set the doll lightly on his back. A
moment passed, the horse still kept his feet.

Kathy slid down from the step-ladder. "Okay, Murray, see
if he will walk."

Murray pulled on the halter. "Giddap, Boy." Root-beer
didn't move. Murray took an apple from his coat pocket, bit
off a chunk and fed it to the pony. "Come on, Boy, let's go."

The buckskin took one step, then faltered as though he had
finally made up his mind. "Come on, good old Boy." Murray's
voice sounded like a silky hand stroking Root-beer's whole
body. He pulled out a lump of sugar and fed it to the horse.
Root-beer began to walk.

"Oh Murray, he's walking! He's walking!" Kathy waved
both hands in excitement. "Oh Murray, look, the doll is slip-
ping off. She ran to Root-beer's side and tried to balance the
doll, but it began to slide again.

"We'll have to fasten the doll to the blanket or it won't stay
on." Kathy ran to bring safety-pins and finally got the doll
fastened securely to the blanket. "Now, you can let him run.
That doll will stay aboard."

Mike stuck his head out the barn window and guffawed,
"Oh ho-ho-ho, you guys ought to march in the Rose Bowl
Parade. You'd win first prize for the most ridiculous exhibit."

"Oh Mike, hush! If anyone gave prizes for laughing hyenas
you'd win all of them." Kathy had never been more disgusted
with her oldest brother.

Murray grinned. "I suppose this whole business must look
plenty funny, but if we succeed, then we'll give old Mike the
horse-laugh." He opened the corral gate. "We'll walk Root-
beer the rest of this afternoon with the doll for his rider. Tomorrow we'll try the saddle, and the next day you'll be the
doll, Kathy."

The next day they put a saddle on the buckskin and walked
him for an hour. Then Murray decided to leave the saddle on
him and let him graze by himself the rest of the day. After

supper they took off the saddle and rewarded the pony with many caresses and kind words, also with apples and sugar.

Next morning the saddle went on again and Root-beer grazed through the morning hours.

Murray hurried through his dinner that day and punched Kathy to remind her that the time had come to work with Root-beer again. She knew what he wanted, excused herself and followed him to the corral. "Should I bring the doll and try her in the saddle first?"

"No, you couldn't pin her to this leather saddle."

"You got the sugar cubes?"

"Yeah, and apples, too, in my pocket." Murray set the step-ladder in place so Kathy could mount the pony easily. Inside the corral gate, they stood and watched Root-beer for a few minutes.

"You know, he really is a beauty." Murray whistled. The buckskin lifted his head, pricked up his ears and trotted over to his young master. Murray put both arms around the horse's neck and laid his freckled cheek against Root-beer's mane. Then he reached into his pocket and brought out sugar. "Now, Kathy, this is it. Climb on easy."

"I just know he'll lie down," Kathy hesitated. "It'd be too good to be true — I mean, if he really held me up."

"All aboard, Kathy." Murray patted Root-beer's neck. "Come along, Boy, we're off with the living doll."

Kathy sat so lightly in the saddle, so lightly that she scarcely breathed or moved. Then she whispered in an awed voice. "He hasn't folded up yet. Oh, Murray, he hasn't folded up yet! See if he'll walk."

Murray pulled on the halter and Root-beer walked. It seemed to Kathy that he held his head higher, looked smarter and more happy. "Oh Murray," she said as Murray unfastened the corral gate, "Do you think he's cured?"

"I think he is cured," Murray smiled and his red hair seemed to flame like sunshine and every freckle on his face twinkled like decorations of some kind.

"Whoopee! Whoopee!" Kathy shouted. "Lead him over by the house so Mother and Daddy can see."

No Rose Bowl Parade ever drew a more enthusiastic audience, Kathy felt sure of that. "I just can't believe my eyes!" Daddy made as though he would faint from shock. Mother and the boys stood by smiling and praising Root-beer and his young trainers.

Kathy slid down into Daddy's arms. "Murray did it, Daddy. You can't know how patient he's been. He knew just how to handle Root-beer." She spoke the words in a loud voice so all the boys could hear. Then she whispered to Daddy. "Aren't you glad we gave them one more chance?"

"I sure am," Daddy whispered back. "Murray has saved Root-beer from the glue factory or the dog-food packers. I suppose it's too soon to tell what Murray has been saved from, something worse probably, but the horse has helped him. That's plain to see."

Then Daddy took Murray by the hand in front of all the boys. "You have done a wonderful job, my boy. The horse is yours, now, your very own."

With a shout of joy, Murray leaped into the saddle and rode away down the road on his own buckskin pony. Kathy watched him go and wondered if he could possibly be happier than she.

As the family walked into the house, Kathy saw that peculiar dreamy look come into Daddy's eyes — that special look which meant that he had some big important thoughts turning round in his head.

"You know?" He spoke almost as though to himself. "If a horse can change a boy like that Murray, maybe . . . ."

"What do you mean, Daddy?" Kathy asked.

"Yes, what do you mean?" Mother echoed.

"I'm thinking about Pom Pom. We know now that Pom Pom has show-horse ability. Look at his Walla Walla performance. If we could show him on Television, thousands of boys and girls could see him and love him and he could help them just as Root-beer has helped Murray."

"A wonderful idea, Daddy . . . ."

He interrupted her. "Such a program will bring in money, too."

"But one doesn't get on Television just by wishing." Mother reminded them. "You'll have to do something."

"Right," Daddy agreed. "I can at least try. T. V. Stations audition new talent all the time."

"Where?" The whole group breathed the word like a prayer.

"Sacramento is the closest city. I'll try there first. We can work out a kiddies' program based on the points we have tried to teach Murray and the other boys, health habits, reverence, church attendance, good grooming, courteous manners and so on. Maybe we could have 500 points. That's a good round number."

"Buck Weaver's 500 program," Mother suggested.

"Better yet, stretch it out to Buckaroo 500. Buckaroo means bronco-buster or a cowboy," Daddy said.

"I've go it! I've got it!" Kathy sang out. "The Buckaroo 500 Program featuring Pom Pom the trained stallion."

"That's it! That's it, Kathy." Daddy caught her up in his arms and danced about the yard.

Just then Murray came galloping into the yard on Rootbeer. He stopped beside the group near the house, reached his hand to Kathy and mounted her behind him, they whirled away into the sunset.

CHAPTER 10

Two Stars

Early the following morning, Daddy set off for Sacramento with Pom Pom. He intended to audition for a television program and see if he couldn't get the Buckaroo 500 program on one of the Sacramento stations.

Kathy begged to go along, but Mother said a firm "No. No, you can't go this time, Kathy. For an audition there must be only your Daddy and Pom Pom."

Kathy accepted this disappointment for one reason only. She would never do anything to hinder Pom Pom in becoming a show-horse.

All that day she worked and played hard to make the hours pass. Evening seemed a long time coming. She felt sure that Daddy would telephone some time after dark to let them know how his audition had come out.

The whole family were eating supper when the telephone rang and Mother ran to answer it. Kathy heard her speak Daddy's name and ran to hold her ear close to the telephone, but all that came through to her was a garbled noise.

Mother hung up. "Oh Mother, was it Daddy? What did he say? Did he get on the T.V. Program?" Every boy had a question and Kathy had a dozen.

"Wait, wait." Mother held up both hands. "I'll tell you all I know. The connection wasn't good and I didn't hear well, but I did make out that Daddy won't be home until very late,

tonight. He said something about 'Channel Thirteen' and then we were disconnected."

"Oh, Mother, how can we wait till morning?"

Kathy wanted to stay up until Daddy came home, but her tired eyes refused to stay open and it seemed eight minutes rather than eight hours later when she opened them to a fresh new morning.

She leaped out of bed and hurried to Mama and Daddy's bedroom. Daddy lay there in a deep quiet sleep. Poor Daddy, he must have gotten home very late in the night.

She heard Mother in the kitchen and raced to her side. "Oh Mother, what did Daddy tell you? Did he sign up with some T.V. station?"

"Yes, he did, Kathy, with Channel Thirteen in Sacramento. He and Pom Pom will have a half-hour show once a week for thirteen weeks. His first program will be next Wednesday."

Kathy danced about the kitchen shouting, "Pom Pom's going to be a T.V. star and everyone will love him."

"I hope so," Mother smiled at Kathy's wild antics. "It's a good time to begin now, summer and no school. You youngsters will have to help Daddy all you can. This T.V. program is going to be an extra burden he will have to carry."

"Oh, I'll help him. I'll go with him every time. I'll help take care of Pom Pom and . . ."

"That isn't exactly what I meant." Mother looked serious. "What about all the work Daddy does around the ranch? Who is going to help with that?"

"The boys, of course," Kathy said. "I have to be with Daddy and Pom Pom."

Mother smiled. "I guess maybe that's true," she said.

By the time Kathy had dressed, Daddy was up. She ran and threw both arms around him. "Oh Daddy, Mother told me. Isn't it wonderful? May I go with you and Pom Pom on Wednesday?"

"Well, Sweetheart," Daddy held her tight. "I couldn't very well get along without you. I hereby make you my production

They saw the light on the camera turn red. The Buckaroo 500 Show was on the air.

manager."

Daddy looked at the boys filing in for breakfast. "I'll need a couple boys too, maybe Mike and Chuck will do. There will be a lot of work to do before Wednesday."

Such a confusion of voices arose around the breakfast table in discussion of the proposed T.V. program that Daddy finally held up his hand. "Silence!" he shouted over the noise. "Don't let all your energy run out your mouths. You are going to need it right now."

The next few days swept by in a bustle of activity and preparation for the television adventure. Daddy drilled Pom Pom on his tricks several hours every day, while the boys managed the ranch work with hearty good will.

Although Kathy felt that Wednesday would never come. It finally did and the caravan left the ranch before day-break. They reached the Television studio in Sacramento an hour before show-time. All the people around the studio seemed to be helping with the last minute preparations. Kathy helped Daddy carry out the camera-man's instructions.

Electricians set up the portable klieg lights and tested them. Then an announcer told them that the show would be on the air in five minutes.

Kathy felt her whole body turn to a bundle of nervous shivers. Would Pom Pom perform like he did at Walla Walla? Would Daddy be nervous, too? She stepped out in front of the cameras as Daddy whispered a few gentle words of comfort to Pom Pom.

Pom Pom nudged her as though to say, "I'm sure glad you're here with me." Kathy took out her pocket comb and combed out the pony's fluffy white tassel. With her handkerchief she wiped the sleep from Pom Pom's eyes.

The one-minute warning came clear and loud. She backed out of the way and smiled at Chuck. They saw the light on the camera turn red. The Buckaroo 500 show was on the air.

Kathy stood with her two brothers and watched Daddy put Pom Pom through his tricks. The wonderful pony seemed to have no fear of cameras or lights, or the crowds of children. He performed as well as though he were alone with Daddy in his home corral.

When the light went out, Kathy could hardly believe that a half hour had passed. She ran to Daddy. "That thirty minutes must be the shortest that ever was."

"It may have seemed short to you." Daddy pushed back his cowboy hat and wiped the sweat from his forehead. "It sure seemed plenty long to me." He sat down on a bale of hay. "Now I'll tell you what I want you to do, you and Chuck. I will buy you both cowboy outfits and next week you can help me on the show."

"Oh, I'd like that better than anything." Kathy felt something in her middle doing handsprings. "What can we do?"

"You can ride Pom Pom and let him buck you. Chuck can be general helper and keep the microphone cables from under my feet. Go bring Chuck and Mike. We'd better start home."

She found the boys in the control room talking with the engineer. The boys' eyes bugged out as they listened to him explain the dials and levers on the panel in front of him. About nine small television screens had been set into the panel. "You see, boys, I'm the one who controls which screen picture goes on the air."

Kathy saw that the boys were so interested in what the engineer told them that they hadn't seen her. She found it hard to turn herself away, but she did. She punched the two boys and told them to come. Then she ran.

When the boys caught up with her, she told them about Daddy's new idea of having them help on the show. "He's going to buy us cowboy outfits and he wants us on the show next Wednesday."

"Boy, oh boy! I'm going to ...."

The loud speaker interrupted Chuck, paging Buck Weaver. Daddy ran toward them, threw Pom Pom's halter rope into Chuck's hands and said, "Load up fellows, while I see what the manager wants."

By the time Daddy rejoined them, the pony had been load-
ed and all the gear stowed in the truck. Kathy saw the pleased
look on Daddy's face. "What is it, Daddy? What did the manager tell you?"

"Well, folks, the manager liked our performance. Says he's
already gotten several phone calls praising our program. Some
came in during the show."

Kathy jumped into Pom Pom's trailer and hugged him tight.
"You are a hit, Pom Pom! You are a hit! I'm so proud of you."

"All right, you kids, you did a fine job of loading. Now hop
aboard." Daddy's voice had a proud ring that Kathy had
never heard before. "Are you all going to ride home in Pom
Pom's trailer?"

"I'd like to if there was any place to sit." Kathy said.

"Sit on the floor." Mike started to close the trailer door.

Kathy heard a tap on the window and saw Daddy motion-
ing to her. She tumbled out and climbed into the cab. "I don't
want our television star to get lonesome, Daddy." She snuggled up close to Daddy, so the two boys could crowd in.

"Your legs would get cramped, Honey, and Daddy would
be lonesome for you."

Kathy thought for a minute. "Well, you are a T.V. star, too.
Guess I'll be glad to sit by you."

They pulled out of the studio grounds and Daddy drove
past the capitol building. The children craned their necks
and exclaimed with surprise and pleasure over the beautiful
buildings and well-kept grounds.

"Now, Kathy, you watch for the road signs. We want to
follow hi-way 40. You try to spot every sign and guide me
through this heavy traffic."

Kathy managed her job so well that the Weaver outfit hit
the four-lane hi-way in a few minutes. Dad looked at his gas
gauge and pulled into the next gas station to refuel.

"Why don't you call Mother and let her know the good
news." Kathy said.

"I'll do that."

While the truck was being serviced, Daddy made a direct call to the ranch, told them how successful the show had been and about what time they expected to reach home.

As he hung up, the station attendant had just finished screwing the cap on the gas tank, "All set. Good luck, Mister."

"I bet Mother was glad to hear your voice, Daddy."

"She sounded real pleased, Kathy, says she and the boys are making a freezer of ice cream and a huge cake, so we can celebrate when we get home."

Chuckles of delight came from the two boys. Kathy clapped her hands and wondered if ever, ever in all her future life she would be so happy again.

They approached the mountains and Daddy stepped down hard on the gas pedal. They started the long pull up to Donner's Pass. All three children drowsed. At the Nevada State line Daddy wakened them. "Look alive, my fellow stars," he said. "We'll be home in two hours. Now is a good time to talk over what we'll do on the show next Wednesday."

The rest of the way home suggestions flew back and forth in the truck cab and by the time they rolled into the home drive, the plans for next Wednesday's show were complete.

All the ranch boys, together with Mother and all the dogs, waited on the lawn with three five-gallon ice cream freezers in their midst. Three huge cakes waited on a white covered card table. As soon as Pom Pom had been cared for, the party began. Such jubilations had never rocked the Weaver ranch before. When it ended, a cast of tired T.V. stars tumbled into bed and slept straight through the summer night.

Week after week the Buckaroo 500 show journeyed from the Nevada ranch to Sacramento. As summer vacation drew to an end, so did the contracted time of the T.V. program. The last of the series fell on the first Wednesday of September.

A few minutes before the show began they brought Pom Pom into the main studio. The manager shook hands with Daddy and the three children. "You've given us a good series, Buck," he said. "We're ready to sign a contract for a second series any time you say."

Eager children began to fill the studio and crowded around Pom Pom and Daddy. "I think we'll just hole up at the ranch for the winter," Daddy told the manager. "Next spring we'll be interested."

"As you like," the manager said. "We're ready any time."

He turned to the crowd of children. "I guess you'll all be going back to school now. Good luck, all of you. Over there on the table is a big watermelon. It's for everyone. Help yourselves."

Kathy led the way to the watermelon. The manager's secretary cut the melon and served them to the children on paper plates. Kathy and the two boys each took a piece. Kathy picked up a salt-shaker and sprinkled her piece of watermelon. She invited all the waiting children to share the melon. "It's sweet and cold."

The manager's secretary suggested that, since the Buckaroo 500 show would begin in a few minutes, they'd all better wait with the watermelon until the show was over. Kathy looked at the studio clock and agreed. She put her half-eaten wedge of watermelon on the table and hurried to join Daddy and Pom Pom.

The program began and Kathy saw that Daddy seemed to be putting special punch into it today — the last appearance for the season.

Kathy did her best, too, and when the red light on the television camera dimmed, she found it hard to believe that this wonderful adventure had ended for a few months.

Everyone dashed for the watermelon. Pom Pom must have smelled it. Kathy heard him call. She shared her piece with him. He gobbled it down and begged for more. The delighted children fed him bits of their pieces. He seemed to relish the rinds most of all.

Everyone said "Goodbye" to everyone else and the Weaver Ranch crowd climbed aboard the new truck which now had a picture of Pom Pom painted on its side advertising the Buckaroo 500 show.

At the last minute the manager ran out and shook hands with Daddy once more and said. "I've been thinking it over and I want to offer you a contract for a daily show next season."

Kathy saw Daddy's eyebrows arch upward in surprise. "That means we'd have to find a place to keep Pom Pom here in Sacramento. Traveling back and forth wouldn't do for daily programs."

"Well, we're ready any time. So long. Good luck."

For the last time this year Daddy shifted gears and the truck lurched off toward Nevada and home. Kathy wiped away a few tears.

Donner's Pass lay just ahead. Even though the hi-way stretched smooth as a floor ahead of them, the truck seemed to sway in a strange way. Kathy looked back through the cab's window into Pom Pom's compartment. He seemed to be straining on his halter.

"Pom Pom sure seems restless, Daddy." Kathy still gazed back at the pony. "He seems to be swaying back and forth. Maybe that's what makes the truck lurch."

Mike pulled Kathy down in the seat. "Aw, sit still, wiggleworm, these curves'd make anybody sway. I feel dizzy myself."

Kathy watched Daddy's face. He looked thoughtful. "You know I felt this jarring and jolting back there on the smooth straightaway stretch of hi-way."

Kathy felt as though an icy hand was squeezing everything inside her chest. She struggled free of Mike's hands and looked back at Pom Pom again. "Oh Daddy, stop! Something's wrong with Pom Pom. He's trying to lie down!"

At the first shoulder on the road, Daddy pulled over and stopped. They all jumped out, Daddy opened the back gate of the fine new truck and looked at Pom Pom. He had slumped half way to the floor. His chest heaved and his breath came out in queer raspy wheezes. Daddy tried to get him to his feet, but he fell to the floor.

"He wants to roll, Dad, and there isn't room." Chuck said.

Kathy tried to say something, but such a big knot pushed up in her throat that nothing could come out — not a word — not a sob. For the first time in her life, Kathy knew a hurt too terrible for cries or tears. Pom Pom must be dying.

"Into the cab quick, kids. Pom Pom's sick and we've got to get him home fast." Daddy grabbed the steering wheel like it was a gun and he pressed down the gas feed as far as he dared.

"What do you s'pose made him sick?" Mike asked. "He sure looks like he's hurtin' awful bad."

"I haven't the slightest idea." Kathy had never seen Daddy look so worried. "It has to be something he's eaten."

Kathy looked back and saw Pom Pom writhing in pain. Oh dear God, is Pom Pom going to die? And just when he's a television star and giving so many people pleasure?

CHAPTER 11

One Terrible Night

The watermelon Kathy had eaten in the television studio began to trouble her stomach. As the Weaver truck careened along the mountain road rushing desperately toward home with the sick pony, Kathy was sure she had reached the bottom of all suffering, but she found that an ache in her stomach did make her still more wretched.

"Oh Daddy," she leaned against him. "Could watermelon make Pom Pom sick? I fed him quite a lot there at the studio and the other children fed him some too. He liked it so much he begged and begged for it."

Daddy looked still more troubled. "Oh, Kathy, watermelon isn't good for horses. We are really in for trouble. I'll call the vet as soon as we get home."

"Hurry, Daddy, hurry!" Kathy moaned, so sick herself and so worried about her pony that she wondered if she would die. If Pom Pom died, she knew that she would too. "Hurry, Daddy, hurry!"

"We can't break the speed limit, Kathy, and we are still a long way from home. It isn't safe to go any faster."

Chuck looked back at Pom Pom. "He's all sprawled out now, Daddy. Do you think we ought to stop?"

"No, Chuck, we can't do a thing for him here on this desert road. We're going as fast as we can. I doubt that anyone has made this trip so fast before."

Hours seemed like days and minutes like hours, but at last the familiar driveway came in sight. Daddy drove the truck right up to the barn and backed the rig up to the open door. He jumped out. "Chuck, run and tell Mother to call the vet and tell him to rush. Mike, bring me some warm soapy water in a wash basin. Kathy, how do you feel now?"

"I feel better, Daddy, now that we're home and can do something for Pom Pom."

"Do you feel well enough to call the boys to help me get Pom Pom out of the truck?"

Kathy didn't answer, she flew to call the boys and they came running from every direction. They swarmed around Pom Pom and almost carried him into the barn and laid him down on a bed of clean straw.

Mother came running out. "I've called the vet and he'll be here in just a few minutes," she said.

Kathy hid her face in Mother's apron and sobbed out loud. "It's all my fault, Mother, I fed him the watermelon because he liked it and when the other kids saw me do it, they fed him some too."

Mother stroked Kathy's hair and comforted her with loving words.

The boys brought hot water and towels. Daddy put hot packs on Pom Pom's belly. Chuck burst into the barn. "The vet's here, folks, get out of the way."

Daddy explained to the doctor about the watermelon and the wild ride home. He set down his satchel and turned the upper lid of Pom Pom's left eye back. "There's congestion in his stomach all right. We'll have to get some pills and some oil into him. If he won't swallow them we'll have to pump his stomach."

As the doctor worked over the pony, Pom Pom began to roll from side to side. "Let him up, boys. It's better for him to walk and exercise himself while I get the oil ready."

A dozen boys helped the doctor give the pony the proper medicine. Then the vet stood up and spoke to Daddy. "This

"Could watermelon make Pom Pom sick? I fed him quite a lot . . . . . "

horse will have to be walked all night, Buck. He can't be allowed to lie down and roll. That will tangle his intestines and kill him. You'd better work in shifts."

"It's my fault." Kathy broke away from the shelter of Mother's arms. "It's all my fault, so I will walk him."

"Not until you have had some rest, my little girl. This has been a terrible day for you." Mother led Kathy toward the house.

Just outside the barn door Kathy looked back at her suffering pet. She broke away from Mother and ran to Pom Pom. She threw her arms around his neck and cried. "Pom Pom forgive me. I didn't mean to hurt you. Please get well." Then she ran back and buried her face again in Mother's apron.

The vet picked up his satchel. "Well, folks, that's all I can do tonight. If he's still alive by morning, give me a ring and I'll stop by and have another look at him."

Mother helped Kathy undress and listened to her evening prayer. "Now, Kathy, you have put your pony in God's hands. Don't worry. All of us do foolish things sometimes. God is able to deliver us even from the results of our own folly."

Kathy crawled into bed. "You will waken me, Mother, so I can take my turn walking Pom Pom?"

"I'll set your alarm clock right now for three o'clock. That will give you several hours rest and maybe Pom Pom will be better by that time."

"They are walking him in one-hour shifts, aren't they?"

"Yes, that's what your Daddy said. Now don't fret. I'll tell Daddy to expect you on duty at three."

After Mother had left and Kathy turned off her bedside lamp, she tried to sleep, but worry over Pom Pom swept over her in unbearable waves of misery. Then she remembered what Mother had said about God saving fools from the result of their foolishness. She lit her lamp again and got her Bible. By looking in the concordance in the back, she found the verse in Psalms 107:17-20

Fools, because of their transgression and because of

their iniquities are afflicted. Their soul abhorreth all
manner of meat; and they draw near unto the gates
of death. Then they cry unto the Lord in their trouble, and he saveth them out of their distresses.

The blessed verses with their promise seemed to enfold her
like a warm glow of light. Fools! Fools! Yes, she'd been a fool
all right, but God's promise covered fools too. She turned out
the light and with her Bible clasped tight to her breast, she
relaxed and slept.

The alarm clock's sharp jangle brought her back to reality,
and she remembered Pom Pom. She jumped out of bed and
went to the window. Lights hovered about the barn. Pom
Pom must be alive. She pulled on warm clothing and tiptoed
through the house. She picked her way to the barn guided
by the faint lantern light that shone from the barn's open
door.

Mike was leading Pom Pom in a wide circle. The circular
trail on the barn floor looked as though it had been worn
smooth with months of use. "All right, Mike, I'll take over
now."

Mike started with surprise and turned toward her. "Why
Kathy, I didn't realize it was three o'clock already."

"Is Daddy here in the barn?"

Mike pointed to a pile of hay where a figure rolled in a blanket seemed to be asleep. "Don't waken him. He is dog-tired.
He's breaking his heart over this pony."

Kathy went over, picked up the lantern and looked into
Pom Pom's face. Pain shone out of his eyes. His whole body
looked limp, shrunken and bedraggled. Beautiful Pom Pom!
Television star and beloved pet, what a miserable change one
night of sickness had made.

"How's he doing, Mike? Has he had a good night?"

"Bad night, I'd say. It's really tough trying to keep him on
his feet. He keeps stopping and trying to lie down. I suppose
the poor fellow is dead-tired." Mike never paused in his move-
ment around the circle. "Can't let him lie down. You heard

what the vet said."

"I can manage him." Kathy reached for the halter rope. "It seems chilly to me in here. Do you suppose Pom Pom needs a blanket?"

"I don't think he needs it yet, Kathy. Feel of him. He's still hot with fever. A blanket might make him sweat more and catch cold."

Kathy began the slow pacing around the circular trail. "Go on to bed, Mike. We'll be okay."

"I'm asleep on my feet." Mike yawned and stretched. "I don't like to leave you alone with him. If he got down, how would you get him up?"

"I'd wake Daddy." Kathy began to grow impatient. "Go on. Pom Pom will do exactly what I say."

Mike staggered out the barn door and Kathy heard his slow footsteps echo along the path to the house. She felt the darkness from the night outside press in about her like a heavy frightening weight. She began to talk to the pony. "You're going to be all right, Pom Pom. You're going to be better in the morning."

Kathy couldn't see that her chattering comforted the pony, but it helped her to keep awake. If only the dark wasn't so big and quiet. She could hardly resist the urge to waken Daddy and that would be a cruel thing to do.

Then she heard a step along the path. Mike must have decided to come back. She'd have to really get tough with him. But as she fixed her eyes on the door, Murray appeared. He carried a big mug of steaming chocolate.

"Oh Murray, you are an angel! I was wishing for a hot drink so much, but I daren't leave Pom Pom. He could die, you know, if some one wasn't here every minute." She kept on walking around the circle.

"Here, let me take over while you drink your chocolate." Murray took the rope from her hands.

Through the rest of Kathy's hour-long shift, Murray stayed with her, encouraging both Pom Pom and Kathy with hopeful words. "I'm sure Pom Pom is going to be all right. You know a bad stomach-ache is a terrible thing. But you know what I think? I think if he'd a been going to die, he'd be gone by now. I reckon he's through the worst."

When Peter came to relieve them at four o'clock, Murray handed him the halter-rope. "I do think the pony's a little brighter, don't you, Kathy?"

"He sure isn't any worse. I can say that." Kathy sighed.

Kathy went back to her room and crawled into bed to catch a little more sleep before the house began to stir at breakfast time. Bless that Murray! No one else would have thought of the hot chocolate and the lonely Kathy. Thank God Daddy hadn't sent him away.

When the vet drove up in the morning, Kathy had already dressed and stood waiting for him at the barn door.

"Well, I see the old boy is still alive." He laid his hand on Pom Pom's rump. "Fever is down. I wouldn't have expected this turn for the better. Someone around this ranch has been praying. Could it be you, young lady?"

"Everybody on this ranch has been praying, doctor." Kathy hid her face in Pom Pom's tassel. "Will he really make it now, do you think?"

"Not out of danger yet, but he has passed his crisis. Better keep him walking till noon, just to be on the safe side." He gave the pony a shot and left.

When Pom Pom's ordeal of walking finally ended and he could lie down in his stall, Kathy nursed him with more tender loving care than she had ever devoted to Seven-up in all the years of her devoted love. Pom Pom improved every day.

The late fall rains fell, green grass began to spring again. The sun seemed about to chase Old Man Winter out of the valley for good. New life entered into Pom Pom. The spring came back into his step. The luster came back to his coat. Again his white tassel glistened with health and his eyes shone with roguish mischief.

Kathy reminded Daddy of the spring television series. "Do

you suppose he remembers his tricks?"

"We are going to find out today." Daddy began to give Pom Pom the old signals and commands. He remembered almost every one.

"Do horses have better memories than people?" Kathy asked.

"This one seems to have a remarkable memory." Daddy had made a special box with colored wooden blocks for a new trick. Pom Pom must learn to choose blocks according to color.

Daddy decided to teach Pom Pom a most important trick. He told Kathy to sit on the corral fence and watch while he tried to teach the pony to come on command.

Root-beer and Pom Pom had both been kept in the big corral during spring pasturing and Root-beer had become a great pet. He craved attention for himself and constantly got in the way.

"Come on, Kathy, let's get Pom Pom out in the open. We'll put a long rope on him and be rid of Root-beer's botheration."

Daddy led Pom Pom through the corral gate into the open desert behind the corral fence. He dropped the end of the rope and commanded the pony to "Come here."

For a couple turns, Pom Pom made a show of following directions. On the third call, he raced wildly for the open country. Like a wisp of smoke, he sailed away on the spring wind.

Both his trainers gave chase.

"Oh, Daddy, I'm out of breath. I can't go anymore." Kathy slowed down and so did Daddy. "What made him pull a trick like that?"

"Just feeling gay, I guess. All that pampering during the winter has got him so full of beans he's about to burst. Daddy puffed for a minute.

They watched Pom Pom, tail waving, mane flying, race toward the distant desert. "Look, Kathy, you run back and have Murray saddle Root-beer and ride back here as fast as you can. I'll try to keep him in sight. If you don't see me when you come back, listen for my whistle."

Daddy went racing off after the flying Pom Pom. Kathy turned back and ran toward the ranch. At the corral fence, she turned to look behind her. Both Daddy and Pom Pom had disappeared.

She found Murray playing with his pet snake, grown now to twice its original size. "Come quick, Murray. I need you."

"What's the matter?" He thrust the snake back into its jar and screwed on the lid.

"Pom Pom's taken off on a wild chase across the desert. Daddy is after him — on foot. Come, saddle Root-beer and let's go."

Murray's hands moved with skilled grace. In a minute he had bridled and saddled the buckskin and leaped into the saddle. He pulled Kathy up behind him. "Hang on tight!" he yelled, and took off across the desert spurring Root-beer to sudden speed.

They ran for a couple miles, then Root-beer, who had grown fat and lazy under Murray's tender care, slacked his pace. Murray drew him to a halt. Both children shaded their eyes and searched the horizon. "Now where do you suppose they've got to?"

"I don't know." Kathy held up both hands to shut out the blinding sun. Daddy said if we couldn't see him to listen for his whistle."

"Well then, let's listen."

A long listening time gave back no sound. "I think we'd better do some hollering." Murray shouted as loud as he could. Kathy joined him on his second yell and their combined howl rang like an Apache warcry through the desert sagebrush and sandhills.

They paused and a faint whistle came back to them. Kathy scanned the horizon again. "Oh, there he is!" Kathy pointed to an outcropping of rocks far off to their right. Daddy stood on a rock and waved a white handkerchief.

"Let's go!" Murray turned Root-beer's nose toward the distant rocks. They drew up close enough to Daddy to reach out and touch him. Kathy could see how tired he was. "Where's Pom Pom?"

"He's off yonder, somewhere among those rocks." Daddy pointed East. "Kathy, you stay here. Let Murray go on and try to catch him."

"Oh Daddy, I have to go. I'll have to ride Pom Pom back."

Daddy managed a wry smile. "If you catch him," he said. "Go on!" He waved them away.

When they reached the rocks Daddy had pointed out, Kathy spotted the runaway. "There he is. Let's go after him. He's just standing there, resting."

Pom Pom saw his pursuers coming and broke into a fresh spurt of galloping. "The rascal!" Kathy felt annoyed with the pony's naughty trick, but she could not help thinking how lovely he looked with his flying mane and tail and the winged swiftness of his four graceful feet.

"We'll just have to chase him." Murray urged Root-beer who seemed to get the idea of a chase when he saw Pom Pom. He gladly galloped after Pom Pom.

The pony had tired himself and his last burst of speed proved short and quickly ended. Even so, he managed to keep out of Murray's reach for another three or four miles. They came close enough so Kathy could call, "Stop, Pom Pom. Stop, I say!" The pony looked around and danced away, just out of reach.

Murray loosened his lasso from the saddle horn and flung it neatly over Pom Pom's head and he came to a full stop. Murray held him while Kathy gathered up his dragging halter rope and gave it to Murray. He waited until Kathy had leaped onto Pom Pom's back and then led the naughty pony back to the rocks where Daddy waited.

Pom Pom stood meekly while Daddy scolded him, then took sugar from his pocket and fed him. Daddy rode on Root-beer with Murray while Kathy took Pom Pom home. The chase had taken three and a half hours.

After that, Daddy trained Pom Pom in the corral while Kathy and Murray exercised Root-beer. The pony mastered new tricks and polished up his old ones.

At last came the night when everything stood ready for the trip to Sacramento on the morrow. The time had come for starting the new television series.

CHAPTER 12

Kathy's Grandest Birthday

Every inhabitant of the Weavers' Boys' Ranch stood in the drive around Pom Pom's truck saying goodbyes to Daddy and the three young television actors, off on their new adventure.

Pom Pom, in perfect health and high spirits, seemed as eager as the other stars to be on his way.

This time the Buckaroo 500 Show would be a daily instead of a weekly affair and when Kathy said goodbye to Mother, she remembered that she wouldn't see Mother for a whole week. A few tears fell.

The rig rolled along the sunny hi-way for several miles. Then gradually they drove into a gray overcast. Kathy thought of her sweater in the cab and pulled it on. The weather seemed to have turned suddenly cold.

Rain began to pelt down and Daddy turned on the heater and the windshield wipers. They followed hi-way Number 40 up, up as it wound up the Sierra toward Donner's Pass.

"Look, Daddy," Kathy pointed. "The windshield wipers leave a clean glass. That isn't rain. It's snow."

"It sure is." Daddy looked worried and turned on the defroster. "It's hard to see ahead and this road is mighty slippery."

"I thought it felt a lot colder," Mike shivered. "How can it snow now? It's practically spring."

111

A pale little boy leaped forward to claim his Shetland pony.

"Not unusual for this elevation, is it, Dad?" Chuck wiped the inside of the windshield with his handkerchief. "Boy, it's sure coming down."

Daddy stepped cautiously on the brake. "Looks like a road-block ahead."

A hi-way patrolman walked up to the driver's window. Dad rolled it halfway down. "Chains are required from this point on. Do you have a set?"

"We don't," Daddy admitted.

"You can buy them at the filling station a half mile back. You just passed it."

Daddy turned the truck around and went back to the filling station, bought a set of chains and put them on the rear tires of the truck. The snow whirled down faster. When Daddy had finished with the chains, his jacket glistened with new-fallen flakes. He jumped into the cab and drove to the road-block. The policeman saw him, smiled and waved him on.

Daddy shifted into low gear for the climb to the summit while the snow fell faster and thicker. Pom Pom began shifting around in his compartment. Kathy knew he must be rest-less and frightened, because of course he couldn't understand about the cold and the snow.

Near the summit, the snow fell in bunches and chunks and drifted deep along the hi-way. Darkness had settled down and made the road ahead hard to see.

Daddy peered through the windshield and slammed on the brakes. "Stalled cars ahead." He got out to see what trouble might be holding them up. Kathy peered out the open door and saw red lights flashing ahead. They threw an eerie light into the snow-choked blackness. Then she saw Daddy running back toward the truck.

"What's the matter, Daddy?"

"We've struck a blizzard. No telling how many cars ahead of us are stuck in the drifts and the snow is coming down faster and heavier than ever. We can't possibly get out of here. I'm afraid we're stuck for the night."

"Oh Daddy, I'm scared. How will we keep warm? What about Pom Pom? Will he freeze to death?" Kathy began to cry.

The relentless snow piled around them and began to bury the truck.

Daddy had disappeared into the dark. Then Kathy saw a mittened hand wipe the snow from the rear window. Then someone opened the door to Pom Pom's compartment. She saw Daddy fill Pom Pom's water bucket with fresh new snow. She wondered if it would be warm enough in there to melt that snow, or if Pom Pom would have to lick it down like an ice cream cone.

Daddy broke open a bale of hay and tossed some of it in around Pom Pom's feet. He checked the exhaust, then made a run for the cab. A blast of cold air came in with him and Kathy hurried to close the door. She coughed.

"Do you think Pom Pom will be all right — not catch pneumonia or anything like that?"

"The snow on top of the truck keeps out the cold, makes the closed compartment like a thermos jug." Daddy started up the engine. "We'll run the motor now and then to get a little heat."

Chuck reached under the seat for a sack. "I'm sure glad Mother sent along a big lot of sandwiches."

Mike smacked his lips. "I sure could eat one of those right now."

Chuck passed the sandwiches around to everyone. They bowed their heads while Kathy offered thanks for the food and asked God to watch over and protect them through the night.

Daddy and the boys ate their bread while Kathy watched the snow fall in wild flurries. A strange, locked-in feeling came over her and she didn't feel hungry.

Chuck finished two sandwiches and yawned. "Think I'll dash back with Pom Pom and stretch out. It'll be a cinch with my sleeping bag."

"Ditto here." cried Mike.

"Go on, boys, but hang onto your hair." Daddy told them. "I'll sit right here behind the wheel and Kathy can sleep in this front seat. Sure hope this blizzard lets up during the night so a snow plow can get through. I've heard that these storms sometimes last for several days."

"I'm sure this storm will stop by morning," Kathy said. "We have prayed about it, you remember."

The two boys climbed into the back of the truck with Pom Pom and were soon asleep. Kathy stretched out on the cab seat and slept too. About midnight she wakened and saw Daddy slumped over the steering wheel.

"Are you asleep, Daddy?"

"I've taken little cat-naps, but I'm awake now."

"Is it still snowing?"

"The snow stopped falling about fifteen minutes ago. The wind has gone down and the sky is clearing. I can see a few stars. If no more snow falls, maybe by morning the snow plows can get through. But don't worry your pretty little head. Go back to sleep."

At daybreak the boys came back to the cab. Kathy sat huddled close to Daddy trying to keep warm. Mike brought his sleeping bag into the cab and spread it over their legs. Kathy felt the warmth from it slowly comfort her. She looked out the window and saw a snow plow coming.

Daddy jumped out and talked to a patrol officer who followed the snow plow. Kathy saw his face brighten and he turned back to the cab. "What's the good news, Daddy?"

"The road will be open for all cars with chains in about ten minutes. The officer is going to let us go first because we have a horse."

Kathy felt a weight lift from her chest. They weren't going to be stuck here on this freezing mountain any longer.

The patrolman motioned Daddy forward. The new tire chains bit into the snow, and the truck lurched forward. Daddy guided it in the tracks of the snow plow. Slowly, cautiously, they inched upward until they topped Donner's Summit.

"We'll make it all right now, won't we, Daddy?"

"We'll get down to Sacramento okay, Honey, but I'm afraid our appointment at the television station is fouled up for sure."

"You mean Pom Pom can't be a television star any more?" Kathy felt a sharp hurt in her middle.

"Well, what would you think if you'd saved a spot on an expensive television show for someone who didn't turn up and didn't notify you?"

"You can explain." Mike spoke up.

"I will try to do that, of course." Daddy still didn't look happy.

"No matter how bad we've had it and no matter what we've lost, we sure haven't had it like the Donner Party had it in the old days." Chuck said. "I guess they were stuck here for weeks and most of them died."

"Yes," Daddy threw a worried look at Kathy. "Yes, we have a lot to be thankful for — paved roads, heated cars and trucks, careful police officers and snow plows. We are all alive and well and not even hungry . . ."

"Wait a minute there," Mike laughed. "Where's that sandwich bag? I'm not so sure about this not-hungry bit."

Daddy drove down the Sierra with great caution. Kathy saw him look at his watch and knew how sorry he must be to have missed that television appointment.

"It couldn't be helped, Daddy. Aren't you thankful we're all alive. Don't you think God knows all about it? Don't you think He will make everything come out right for us?" Kathy took hold of Daddy's arm and spoke so earnestly that he looked down at her with his old smile.

"Of course, Kathy. Someone has said that our disappointments are His appointments."

The miles rolled past fast and faster. Snow gave way to dry hi-way and the skyline of Sacramento loomed before them. Kathy felt a welcome relief when they turned into the television studio's parking lot. Kathy and the boys stayed in the truck with Pom Pom while Daddy went into the studio. He

didn't come out for a long time and when he did, Kathy saw
a puzzled expression on his face.

"What is it, Daddy?"

"A strange development. This station changed management
yesterday. The production manager I made my deal with has
joined Channel Eleven in San Jose, California. I just talked
with him over the telephone and he offers me a fifteen minute spot, five days a week, on an hour-long program for children. It's a clown show. A wonderful Danish clown called
Hocus Pocus is the star of that program."

"That sounds much better than what you had fixed up
here," Chuck said. "Come on, let's head for San Jose."

"Yes, indeed." Daddy shuffled around in the glove compartment and tossed a California map to Kathy. "Here pick out
our route, Kathy. We are on the air this afternoon and we
have a lot of things to tend to before then."

Under Kathy's expert directions, the Weaver truck with its
cargo of hope, and dreams, and Pom Pom, reached San Jose
and soon located the studios of Channel Eleven.

Daddy went into the building and stayed for an hour. He
came out with such a big smile on his face that Kathy knew
something wonderful was about to happen. The hours left
before the afternoon program proved busy indeed. Lodging
had to be found for the stars of the Buckaroo 500 Show and
for the chief star of all, Pom Pom.

When the clown show began, the cast of Buckaroo 500
stood watching in fascinated wonder. Children crowded into
the studio. They swarmed over the jolly clown and the sounds
of their happy voices filled the room. Kathy could hardly
believe it possible that Pom Pom and her Daddy would be a
part of this popular program.

When the moment came for Daddy to lead Pom Pom into
the stage area, the children went wild wih delight.

Laughing and joking in his charming way, Daddy con-
trolled the children while he put Pom Pom through his most
fascinating tricks. By the time the fifteen minutes ended, any-

one could see that the Buckaroo 500 show had caught on.

Weeks went by and Kathy knew that in a few days she would have another birthday. "I know this will be the happiest birthday of all my life," she told Daddy as they got ready to go down to the studio for Pom Pom's television show.

"I'd like to help you make this birthday the nicest you've ever had." Daddy helped her into the truck cab. "What can we do?"

"Let me think about it today, Daddy," Kathy said. "I want to decide right, you know."

At the studio, Kathy watched the children swarm around Pom Pom's corral and beg for rides and kisses from the beautiful pony. She clapped her hands and shouted for joy as Pom Pom entertained the children with his wonderful tricks.

He gives so much pleasure to those children, she thought to herself, yet none of them can possibly be as happy as I am because Pom Pom is my very own horse. Nothing can make a child so happy as having a horse of his own.

"Daddy," Kathy began, after the show ended and they started for home. "Daddy, I've thought of the nicest thing to do for my birthday."

"Now what can that be?"

"You know what my biggest happiness is?"

"Pom Pom, I suppose."

"Right. And I have been thinking today how nice it would be to see other children have horses to make them happy." Kathy took hold of Daddy's hand. "Couldn't we give away a pony on my birthday?"

"What a splendid idea!" Daddy wrinkled his forhead and Kathy knew he must be thinking hard. "You know, we can tie the gift pony right in with the 500 points. We can have a drawing and the child whose name is drawn will get the gift pony."

"That will be just the way I want it." Kathy said.

"Tomorrow I'll announce that we intend to give away a pony. We can give out the cards through shopping centers where we give free rides."

Together Kathy and Daddy went to a horse ranch to pick out a pony. They bought a Shetland colt, pure white, a dream of a pony. All the rest of that week Kathy spent most of her time brushing and petting the little white pony.

"You are my birthday pony," Kathy told her. "You are going to make some child so happy that I will have the grandest birthday I've ever had."

The pony seemed to understand.

The morning of Kathy's birthday found her out of bed, dressed and so excited that she could eat almost no breakfast at all. By eight o'clock she and the pony were at the studio with Daddy.

"This day is the happiest of all my life and getting better every minute." Kathy told Daddy and the boys.

Kathy saw the huge crowd of children and their mothers who waited beside Pom Pom's studio corral for the show to begin. They must have come for the pony drawing.

All through the show, Daddy let the lovely little white pony wander about the corral, so everyone could enjoy seeing her.

At last the moment came for drawing the lucky name.

"Suppose we let Pom Pom draw the card." Daddy said.

Kathy nodded her consent and with his soft lips, Pom Pom carefully drew a name from the box.

"Michael Fverett." Daddy read the name on the winning card. Then Kathy's heart seemed to catch in her throat. A pale little boy limped forward into the corral to claim his prize pony.

"He is lame." Kathy whispered to herself. "What could make him happier than this little white pony?"

Daddy lifted the little boy onto the pony's back.

The little fellow's dancing eyes fairly glistened with delight. He looked back over the fence and Kathy saw his mother standing there crying out loud into her handkerchief — tears of joy.

Daddy told the little boy how to care for his pony, and how

to ride her. He praised him for getting all the 500 points so he could win such a beautiful prize.

"Happy?" Daddy asked Kathy as they left the television studio that day.

"Of course. This birthday is the grandest I ever had."

"I have thought of a way to add just a little bit more joy to your birthday. I have decided that the Buckaroo 500 Show will give a pony away every twenty days after this. Your birthday and your idea started this, Kathy, and you should be pleased."

Kathy threw her arms around Daddy's neck. "This is my dream come true. Ever since Pom Pom stuck his head into my window that first morning he came to our house and ever since I saw how Root-beer changed Murray to a good boy, I've known what a horse can do."

Daddy started the truck. "I take it, you are satisfied with your birthday celebrations, then."

"Daddy, there isn't anything God ever put into this world that can make so much happiness as a horse."

CHAPTER 13

Pom Pom, TV's Wonder Stallion

Buckaroo 500
A N D
-THE REST OF THE STORY-

by Ed Guthero

ittle did Kathy know when Pom Pom had arrived at the youth ranch the previous year, what a multi-dimensional pony he would turn out to be. Nor did she know that within a short time, her Dad, Buck Weaver, would debut on his own television show, Buckaroo 500, along with Pom Pom and a colorful cast of animals. Or that Buckaroo 500 would become a TV favorite for millions of children throughout the United States. Kathy didn't know back then that boys and girls in far-away places such as New York City, Philadelphia, Charlotte, Los Angeles, Kansas City, Salt Lake City, Denver, Portland, Boston, and Chicago would be sitting in their living rooms watching Pom Pom and Buckaroo 500 on the family television set. She had no idea that Buck Weaver, the cowboy host, and his performing critters would strike a chord with viewers across the country. No, Kathy didn't know all that yet; at present Buck and the gang were anticipating only what might happen with their television opportunity in San Jose.

Kathy, with her brothers Mike, Chuck, and Tim, had always

known the joy of caring for animals and the pleasures of rural living in Fallon, Nevada. The Nevada Youth Ranch had proven to be an effective tool for teaching responsibility and citizenship to troubled youngsters. At the ranch everyone was up by 6:00 a.m. There were chores to do, and animal care was the first order of the day. With numerous horses, cows, chickens, and goats there were plenty of animals to be cared for. The ranch quarters could accommodate thirty-two boys.

Kathy had seen how training Rootbeer (called "Maverick" on the show) had helped Murray, and like her Dad, she knew there is a special connection between animals and children.

Maverick had been "high schooled" (an equestrian term meaning to train a horse to do tricks) by Buck, and Kathy also trained Maverick as a show horse, entering him in "stock-seat" equitation, western pleasure, and "open trail" class competitions. With Maverick as her mount, Kathy won more than seventy-five awards in "open trail" class competitions alone. The difficulties of running such an operation were challenging, but the work Buck and his wife, Joan, were doing at the Nevada Youth Ranch attracted the attention of civic leaders around the state. Prominent individuals such as Nevada governor Grant Sawyer and Reno mayor Bud Baker helped conduct fund raising drives for the ranch. In addition, various local ranchers, businessmen, doctors, attorneys, and even television personality Ed Sullivan supported the youth ranch.

• Buck and Kathy's showhorse, Maverick, who also appeared on Buckaroo 500. Maverick is shown here with a special saddle awarded to Buck by the Circle Y saddle company for the Buckaroo 500 TV show.

For five years the Weavers had worked with distressed youth that state judges had sent to their Nevada homestead for rehabilitation. On this ranch Buck had begun his experiments using animals as the "access route" to young peoples' hearts and minds. He would give the kids particular responsibilities as they helped raise and care for the youth ranch animals—chickens, cows, dogs, and both show and work horses. The boys' were allowed to help train the horses as a reward in the merit system that Buck incorporated into the youth ranch program. Las Vegas newspaper reporter Rexton Trembath visited the ranch and wrote in his column: "It has the savor of love and sincerity and a great unselfish effort. . . . I'm mighty proud of Joan and Len (Buck) Weaver and what they're doing for kids from broken homes. . . . (Buck) has assigned himself to a cause that, more often than not, is shunned by society." Buck recognized the bonding that took place between the boys and the horses—and used pony rides and training privileges in his merit system to help them develop.

Years later, Al Dickerson, the third boy sent to the ranch, still calls Weaver, "Dad" and says his experience at the ranch "turned his life around and kept him out of prison." He now owns and successfully operates AD Transportation in San Jose, California. A teenaged ranch alumnus reflects, "At the youth ranch we got the understanding we needed. We were also shown that the biggest help we get in life is the help we give ourselves. As for Mr. Weaver, he's giving boys the hand up we need when we're falling fast."

• *Buck teaches Pom Pom to "play dead," one of the multitude of tricks they performed on Buckaroo 500.*

• *Pom Pom oversees corral activities from his special stall on the Buckaroo 500 set as guest Jack Hansen of KGO-TV San Francisco feeds a calf.*

Buck Weaver knew that caring for animals brought needed responsibility to young people, but he could also see himself in the faces of the restless boys sent to his Nevada ranch. For Buck had also struggled as he was growing up. As a youth, he battled his way to the Nevada State Golden Gloves Boxing Championship. Adulation and alcohol followed, as well as street-fighting and brawling. Buck sought security in toughness, but inside, he knew it wasn't enough.

"I was a good fighter all right, but I couldn't stop fighting when I stepped out of the ring," Buck recalls. "I was a drunk for six years. Then I saw my real self for the first time and decided to do something about it." He re-discovered God and directed his energies into the youth ranch.

The interaction between Buck, Joan, Kathy, Mike, Chuck, Tim, the ranch animals, and troubled boys proved positive. Weaver, his animals, and the boys were often called upon for personal appearances before Nevada Lions', Kiwanis and Rotarian groups. These outings led directly to the first television appearances by Buck, Pom Pom, and the crew. The lessons learned at the youth ranch were key foundations in the development of Buckaroo 500.

When Buck and Pom Pom first arrived in San Jose, they were scheduled to do only a number of five-minute segments on the "Hocus Pocus Show," hosted by the popular Bay-area clown on KNTV/Channel 11. Yet Pom Pom, the trained Welsh stallion quickly became a children's favorite in San Jose and the Lower East Bay area.

Soon Buckaroo 500 developed into a self-contained, quarter-hour show purposely designed to fit into any existing cartoon or children's program. The special chemistry between boys and girls and Buck's animals began working its magic over the air waves and into thousands of Bay-area homes.

In the station's parking lot, the management of KNTV/Channel 11 built a special outdoor set for Buckaroo 500, featuring a ranch corral. A live audience of enthusiastic children ringed the corral, and Buck's performing animals roamed around inside. Buckaroo 500 was now really on its way as an independent children's TV production; there was the possibility of syndication. KNTV program director, Bob Hosfeldt, was pleasantly surprised with the rapid success of Backaroo 500. Just a month after the show went on the air in its 9:00 a.m. time slot, the station's rating book indicated that Buckaroo 500 had become the most successful daytime program in Channel 11's history.

"I must admit that I was highly skeptical of Buckaroo 500 when first approached with the program idea," Mr. Hosfeldt told Buck. "Now I'm a believer! It's unique because it's entertaining, wholesome, and attracts a large loyal audience."

Hosfeldt had seen a lot of children's programs during his career, and he felt the locally produced Buckaroo 500 could compete favorably in any television market in the United States. His opinion would soon prove accurate.

Kathy's wonder stallion, Pom Pom, and Buck, clad in snappy western wear complete with monogrammed leather chaps, became the early focus of the show. Buck and Pom Pom were certainly on the same wavelength; at times it seemed that they even knew what the other was thinking. "That horse and I think alike," Buck laughed.

Using subtle hand motions, with touch and voice commands woven into the program's casual conversational tone, Buck signaled Pom Pom to perform a variety of impressive tricks. The audience of children that sat along the corral fencing during the taping of Buckaroo 500 looked on in wide-eyed amazement as Pom Pom demonstrated his ability in "math class." Buck would call out a combined addition and subtraction problem and the attentive Welsh Stallion would select the correct answer displayed on cards or blocks in the corral. Sometimes the stallion would "paw" the right answer by stomping his foot the correct number of times. Pom Pom truly was a very smart stallion. After all, how may horses can do mathematics?

In addition to his intelligence, Pom Pom developed a flair for comedy. One of the jaunty Welsh stallion's most unique tricks

involved Buck, two "little wrangler" guests, and Pom Pom's saddle blanket. The trick also taught children the importance of wearing a seat belt while in an automobile, with Buck using Pom Pom's bucking rig harness to symbolize a seat belt.

Buck had taught Pom Pom to remove his saddle blanket on a secret command, but, of course, the "little wranglers" didn't know this. He would carefully

• *Another Buckaroo 500 animal star, Sparky (the world's biggest little bucking horse) rears up for world champion bronc rider Paul Templeton, one of the many special guests to visit Buckaroo 500.*

place the blanket on Pom Pom and then tell the two chosen guests, "Don't take this blanket off; make sure it stays on Pom Pom's back."

Then Buck would turn and walk away to retrieve the bucking rig. Immediately, the stallion would whirl around and mischievously snatch the blanket in his teeth—pulling it off and throwing it down. The unsuspecting kids would go to pick up the blanket, only to be confronted by Buck, who had quickly returned.

"Didn't I ask you not to remove Pom Pom's blanket?" Weaver asked seriously.

"We didn't," the bewildered little wranglers would reply.

Then Buck would turn to Pom Pom and ask the stallion if he'd discarded the saddle blanket. Pom would solemnly shake his head side to side, indicating his innocence. Weaver would again put the blanket on his stallion, instruct the guests not to touch it, and again walk away. Sure enough, Pom Pom, the prankster, would quickly snatch the blanket away once more as soon as Buck turned his back. Repeated in quick succession, the trick delighted the audience.

Besides being a mathematician and a prankster, Pom Pom would also buck on command, take a bow, kiss the children, and let them ride him around the outdoor studio corral with as many as six of them on his back at once! Buck would good naturedly warn the "little wranglers" that if a seventh child were to mount the Welsh stallion, Pom Pom would immediately collapse. Of course, the kids pled to add just one more rider, and Pom Pom (who had been trained to lay down in such a situation) would dispatch the riders safely in Buck's direction.

With the television cameras recording events at Buckaroo 500, Pom Pom was quickly becoming a TV star in the eyes of northern California children. Soon boys and girls were enthusiastically sending "Pom Pom, the Trained Welsh Stallion" stacks of fan mail.

"Dear Buck, I'm horse crazy, and I just love Pom Pom. He's such a pretty horse. Will you please send me a picture album of Pom Pom," wrote Vicki, in a letter from Rancho Cordova, California.

"I watch your show everyday," came the word from Lorri Ann in Sacramento. "I would like a picture of Pom Pom. I want to pay this money for the picture because Pom Pom is a nice pony," a quarter was enclosed.

Bay area children also eagerly wrote asking for tickets to be part

of the corral studio audience as Buckaroo 500 continued to draw more and more viewers.

One of the most touching incidents regarding the show involved Johnny Shaw, a loyal first-grade viewer from southern California. Johnny developed serious headaches, and a doctor discovered he had a brain tumor. He said Johnny had about six months to live.

A California radio station heard about the youngster, and in the spirit of today's "Make a Wish Foundation," teamed up with Pacific South West Airlines to offer Johnny a trip anywhere he wanted to go—Disneyland, Sea World, anywhere. Johnny chose to attend a live taping of Buckaroo 500. His greatest wish was to meet Pom Pom and Dixie. Johnny and his parents were flown to the set of Buckaroo 500, and Johnny received a complete "wrangler" outfit—cowboy hat, chaps, boots, and custom shirt. For a whole week of taping— five episodes—the little boy was the special guest on the show. He also stayed at the home site ranch with the Weavers.

It was a special time on the set. Johnny was a wonderful guest, quietly enjoying his wish to be part of the Buckaroo 500 crew. Within a few months, Johnny died, but he was buried in his "little wrangler" outfit, just as he had requested. Buck and Joan became good friends of the Johnny's parents, and his older brother, Tim, grew up to be a medal-winning member of the United States Olympic water polo team.

In an amusing side note concerning the show's loyal fan base, the San Jose Mercury News reported receiving an irate call from a reader complaining that the newspaper had misspelled "Buckaroo 500" in the paper's TV announcement guide. "You said '502;' it should have been '500,' " said a frustrated Debbie Wright.

"What should have been '500?' " inquired a reporter answering the phone.

" 'Buckaroo 500.' You said it was '502,' " Miss Wright shot back, still frustrated.

Just as the reporter checked the listings and was about to apologize for the error, another angry voice (this time from Sandy Wright) broke in and reprimanded the reporter for his carelessness.

Soothing tones did little to comfort the angry voices, and the reporter promised that such an error would never happen again.

After a long silence, the callers wearily said, "Okay"—and hung

• *Buck interviews some "little wranglers" on the set of Buckaroo 500.*

• (Above) Buck and Alex, the Bantam rooster, who would crow on command, especially in approval of the show's sponsor, Wonder Bread. (Right) Ginger was used in advertising spots for All Jersey Milk.

up! The protestors, Debbie Wright and her sister Sandy were only five and four years old respectively. It seems children in the area were taking the Buckaroo 500 show quite seriously!

In addition to Pom Pom, Buck introduced a number of other animal stars to the corral set as the show steadily grew in popularity. There was Alex the bantam rooster, who would perch casually on Buck's arm or on the old-style telephone that was mounted to the barn wall. Alex could crow on command, and often his amusing "cock-a-doodle-doo's" would echo across the corral set. It was the rooster's seal of approval—usually delivered in praise of the show's sponsor, Wonder Bread.

At any given time Buckaroo 500 viewers might be entertained by "Toughfy and Fluffly," the gray geese, Ginger the Jersey Cow, accompanied by various day-old calves, Dee Dee, the owl-faced monkey, baby goats, Willie and Billie, who were always creating havoc, Spike the Bantam rooster, Bantam hens along with their fluffy chicks, Jet-Jet the Pomeranian, who was the "Pie Pop guard" in that sponsor's commercials, keeping kids away from pies. The cast also included a baby deer, Sparky the Shetland Stallion, who could rear and walk on his back legs, Rocky the trained raccoon, Bruno and Bernie, two huge, but lovable, wagon-pulling Saint Bernard dogs, Pom Pom's foals—Cheyenne, Dawn, Fawn, and Candy—and Mig and Mag, the sturdy pony team that pulled the Buckaroo 500 covered wagon. Mig and Mag made numerous appearances with Buck at supermarket parking lots to promote the fast-growing show and its commercial sponsors.

Youngsters welcomed the sight of the long-maned ponies, with cowboy Buck at the reins, hauling the Buckaroo 500 covered wagon unto a neighborhood parking lot, the ponies' hooves clicking against the hard city pavement.

Kathy and her brothers, Mike, Chuck, and Tim, often accompanied their dad on these promotional excursions and saw how city children loved to ride in the wagon and pet the faithful ponies. On such trips to various shopping outlets, children who had seen Pom Pom and his animal friends only on their television sets, had an opportunity to meet them in person. Such contact further established Buckaroo 500's television audience, and the show continued increasing its viewership. Soon Buckaroo 500 was outranking such

• (Left) The lovable St. Bernards, Bruno and Bernie, pull Dixie and Kathy in the wagon as Buck looks on. Kathy is kissing Pom's new baby. (Below left) Singer Jerry Starr recorded the show's theme song on Link Records, just one of many Buckaroo 500 specialty products.

• (Above) Count the legs . . . . A chorus line of "little wranglers" aboard Pom Pom. (Left) The show's pony team, Mig and Mag, driven by Vernon Shaw, a Native American boy from the Youth Ranch, were favorites at California shopping centers.

popular programs as Leave It to Beaver and The Rifleman in KNTV's listings.

A key factor in the show's success—in addition to Buck's "sometimes-too human" animals—was its basic character-building approach that Weaver worked into the show.

In sharp contrast to the slapstick, near frantic pacing, and violent undertones in much of children's TV programming, Buckaroo 500 provided a relaxed, fun-filled setting. Parents appreciated the show's strong (but never preachy) emphasis on "doing the right things." The program title, Buckaroo 500, came from Buck's name combined with a 500-point incentive plan that asked children to keep score on a tiny gold-and-brown Buckaroo 500 membership card that was available at all of the show's advertisers. Viewers received points in three main areas: character, health habits, and devotion. Respectfulness, telling the truth, helpfulness, cleanliness, deportment, and church attendance were encouraged. Each card included the Buckaroo 500 pledge: "I will always do my best."

Combined with the principles of animal care and responsibility proven at the youth ranch, Buckaroo 500's attitude to children's television gave the program a unique edge.

Buck encouraged personal responsibility in the little "wranglers" that visited the corral in person or who viewed the show on their television sets at home. "He rarely talks down to children and never talks down to animals," a television executive observed.

"I wanted to offer an alternative to the early-morning cartoons," Buck said. Thousands of children and parents also liked the option; Buckaroo 500 was on its way to capturing larger audiences than any other TV programs aired prior to 7:00 p.m. in the lower East Bay area!

The interaction between the children and the animals gave the show a feeling of participation for both viewers and corral regulars. Often Buck would hoist a child from the audience over the corral fence to participate in one of his learning experiences or for a ride on Pom Pom's back or just to pet the other animals. Weaver called the Buckaroo 500 children and fans "little wranglers."

"The children's access to the animals in the outdoor, specially-built corral set is one of the basics of Buckaroo 500's television success," Buck pointed out. The other basic factor was the regular

appearance of at least two of the highly-trained animals in his troupe—especially Pom Pom—at every broadcast.

It had taken a lot of work and patience to train Pom Pom, and the Welsh Stallion's keen intelligence and showmanship kept him in the Buckaroo 500 spotlight daily. But after the show's beginning success, another new animal star emerged on the set six months into the show's initial season. It wasn't a typical ranch animal, either. True, it was a dog, and dogs are quite common on rural farms and ranches. But this dog was a Doberman. Dobermans aren't your typical Western side-kicks; they are more at home in the army or guarding industrial buildings than on a ranch.

Other Western television personalities of the era had their dogs. Roy Rogers had "Bullet," a big German Shepherd. And of course, Rusty had "Rin Tin Tin," also a German Shepherd. Well, Buck Weaver and Buckaroo 500 had "Dixie the Doberman," who proved to be very much at "home on the range."

Dixie and her owner, Auntie Beth Hill, showed up unexpectedly on the Buckaroo 500 set one day during an on-air taping of the show. Buck could see that Dixie was a highly intelligent Doberman—well trained and alert—just the type of dog that would make an excellent cowboy side-kick, even if she wasn't a typical Western canine. But Auntie Beth Hill wasn't eager to sell her highly-trained Doberman. Yet, she agreed to lease Dixie to Buckaroo 500 for $100 a week—a five-day taping period during which Buck and the San Jose TV crew could video tape a full week of programs. Buckaroo 500 was being shown on KNTV Monday through Friday, and the show continued its successful climb in the ratings.

A survey of parents in the lower Bay area indicated that Buckaroo 500 was a favorite by a margin of more than six to one in comparison with other children's programming—including live shows and cartoons. It was evident that parents approved of Buck's philosophy that the responsibility of caring for animals was a healthy, happy formula for producing good citizens.

Dixie, the pure-bred Doberman, was a major plus for Buckaroo 500, and Buck wanted her to be a permanent fixture in the Buckaroo 500 corral. "If Auntie Beth would sell her, can we afford to buy the dog?" Buck asked Joan after taping one of their daily shows.

• *A new star on the Buckaroo 500 horizon, Dixie, the world's smartest Doberman.*

• (Above) Dixie feeds a carrot to Cheyenne, Pom's colt. (Right) Pom Pom and Dixie the Doberman became favorites of children across the country who tuned in to watch the colorful antics at the Buckaroo 500 corral.

"How much should we pay Auntie Beth to sell Dixie?" he thought out loud. Joan and Buck decided they'd offer Mrs. Hill $500 for her prized Doberman and held their breaths wondering what her response might be.

The next time Auntie Beth Hill visited the Buckaroo 500 set, the cowboy host anxiously approached Dixie's owner. "How much do you want for her?" Buck asked. He could feel the hope rising in his heart as his words hung in the air. Auntie Beth paused and pondered the cowboy's question.

"Twenty-five hundred dollars total . . . Fifteen hundred dollars for the dog and one thousand dollars to properly transfer the dog's affections. That's my price," she stated.

The words smashed Buck's hopes with a thud, he had expected to pay only five hundred dollars. Buck was disappointed and frustrated. He began to think very un-Buckaroo 500 negative thoughts about Auntie Beth Hill and her extravagent asking price.

Despite the resentment Buck could feel bouncing around in his head, the cowboy host—who had been teaching character-building lessons to Buckaroo 500 viewers for months—was about to learn a lesson himself.

"What a selfish, hypocritical old lady she is," Buck complained to Joan when he returned home. "She's well off and doesn't need the money. She knows how hard we're trying to meet expenses at the station and keep Buckaroo 500 on the air. She knows how much good Dixie can do for the program. How could she ask for so much money for that dog?"

Buck didn't sleep well that night, and His judgments about Auntie Beth gnawed away at him during the following days. Buck wasn't happy, but he continued to lease Dixie for $100 a week. Yet he knew Buckaroo 500 really needed Dixie as a permanent star in his cast of animals. So he made a trip to his local bank to speak with the manager about a loan.

"If you're dumb enough to pay $2,500 for a dog, I'm dumb enough to loan it to you," laughed Paul Rose, the bank manager, who was well aware of Buckaroo 500's positive influence on California children because his own children had been on the show and had met both Pom Pom and Dixie.

A short-time later Auntie Beth quietly approached Buck Weaver.

"I've been praying about this," Auntie Beth began slowly. "I know how you and your director Bob Hosfeldt feel about Dixie as an asset to the show and how the children enjoy her tricks. I've decided to sell her to you, but you need to know that I won't be keeping the money myself."

Buck's eyebrows raised as he learned the real story about Auntie Beth. The person he had judged as selfish was really a kind-hearted woman who had been quietly raising funds with Dixie and her live shows for Christian medical missionaries working along the distant Amazon River in the hot jungles of South America. All the money from the sale of Dixie would go to helping the missionaries buy a boat to aid them in their work, reaching the villages along the great river.

Buck looked down uncomfortably at his cowboy boots. There was a funny feeling in his stomach, and he realized he'd made a big mistake in jumping to conclusions about Auntie Beth's motives. "I was so wrong," Buck now says. "I learned never to judge anyone, not to jump to conclusions about people, and always give them the benefit of the doubt."

So Buckaroo 500 obtained Dixie full time, and today, somewhere along the far-away Amazon, is a river boat named "Dixie" and a jeep named "Pom Pom," bringing help to South American villagers.

Buck billed Dixie as the "world's smartest Doberman," and she dazzled viewers with her ability to perform duties and tricks. She really did seem almost human. Being a very proper Doberman, Dixie faithfully patrolled the Buckaroo 500 corral. And like a true cowboy side-kick, she made sure everything was in the proper place. She'd open and close the corral gate or she'd hold the nursing bottle for a newly-born goat. And like Pom Pom, she was a natural performer. On a single command by Buck, usually obscured in casual conversation, Dixie

• *Kathy looks on as Dixie the Doberman sits amidst her avalanche of fan mail.*

• *Dixie gives Buck a "high five" as actor and war hero Audey Murphy laughs approvingly. The car pictured once belonged to Murphy and was used by Dixie for her personal promotional appearances. Audey Murphy was the most honored and decorated American soldier of World War II.*

would perform not just one trick, but a related series of tricks.

"Dixie, please get my car keys," Buck would say. In order to fulfill this command, Dixie had to (1) go to the desk, (2) open the desk drawer, (3) pick up the keys from the drawer, (4) put them down on top of the desk, (5) close the desk drawer with her nose, and (6) pick up the keys and bring them to Buck.

Upon Buck's command "Dixie, put my keys away," the Doberman would faithfully do the same process in reverse.

This impressive ability to combine a number of tricks in a continuous chain amazed the viewing audiences and became a Dixie trademark. Buck, Pom Pom, and Dixie proved to be quite a trio, and Buckaroo 500 became even more popular.

In the Salinas, Monterey, Santa Cruz, San Jose area Buckaroo 500 was reaching more homes from sign on till 7:00 p.m. than at least thirty other big-name TV shows including Jeopardy, The Price is

Right, Truth or Consequences, Let's Make a Deal, Father Knows Best, As the World Turns, The Edge of Night, General Hospital, Leave It to Beaver, The Rifleman, Webfoot, Yogi, Woody Woodpecker, and even the ABC Early Evening News!

The ARB broadcast report indicated that in San Jose alone, Buck, Pom Pom, and Dixie were being seen in 36,700 KNTV homes and that 53,100 children were sitting in front of television sets tuned into Buckaroo 500 each day. The show's influence had blossomed to such an extent that a commercial on Buckaroo 500 was more expensive than one on the ABC Early Evening News.

The fact that KNTV's Buckaroo 500, in its 9:30 a.m. time slot, could reach more children than a powerful national network show such as Leave It to Beaver (which had the benefit of 5:00 to 6:00 p.m. scheduling) made television executives take notice. The casual informality of Buckaroo 500, its animals, and its learning theme was a bona fide success! It was also very significant that Buckaroo 500 was out-polling the Kellogg cartoon shows by a substantial margin. Even though the nationally shown Webfoot, Yogi Bear, and Woody Woodpecker characters aired at 5:30 p.m. compared to the 9:30 a.m. Buckaroo 500 slot, Buck and his animal friends reached 22,800 more children and were seen in 18,500 more homes than the competing Kellogg cartoon shows.

Television is not only entertainment; it is a business that depends on advertisers buying air time to meet its expenses and turn a profit.

• *Soon Buckaroo 500 was out-ranking popular shows like Leave it to Beaver, The Rifleman, and the Kellogg cartoon shows.*

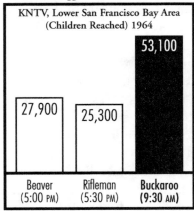
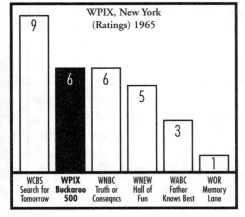

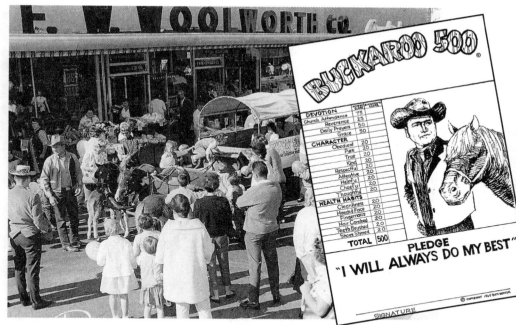

DEVOTION		
	75	
Church Attendance	25	
Reverence	50	
Daily Prayers	50	
Grace		
CHARACTER		
Obedient	20	
Pure	20	
True	20	
Kind	20	
Respectful	20	
Attentive	20	
Helpful	20	
Cheerful	20	
Thoughtful		
HEALTH HABITS		
Cleanliness	20	
Hands & Face	20	
Fingernails	20	
Hair Combed	20	
Teeth Brushed	20	
Shoes Shined	20	
TOTAL	500	

PLEDGE

"I WILL ALWAYS DO MY BEST"

SIGNATURE

• *Whenever the Buckaroo 500 crew would go on promotional appearances at sponsors' retail outlets, crowds of children were sure to gather around.*

Advertisers, of course, want their commercials to be seen on the most popular television shows because that means more viewers will see their product—whether it be milk, bread, or dog food. And Buckaroo 500 was becoming a very popular show. "It's a numbers game," Buck has said. The advertisers and television executives knew that while thousands of Buckaroo 500 fans were watching the show each morning, so were their mothers—mothers who did the family shopping! The basic formula for a television show to be a success is simply this: moving product.

It was an added bonus that not only were the Buckaroo 500 trio entertaining, but Buck, Pom Pom, and Dixie turned out to be "naturals" in television advertising/marketing.

Wonder Bread realized that the positive shenanigans of the Buckaroo 500 threesome was an excellent vehicle for their product and became an early buyer of the show—fifty-two weeks at a time or 260 shows! Arden All Jersey Milk was another advertiser which became a steady buyer of time on Buckaroo 500, as did a number of other bay area companies. In addition, Buckaroo 500 was selected as the advertising vehicle to introduce Eggo waffles and potato chips to the television industry.

Buck, Pom Pom, and Dixie not only encouraged children to build good characters and solid citizenship skills, they could also sell products for the companies that advertised on the show. As a result, the station was happy, the advertisers were happy, and Buck's positive message was reaching children and parents.

This successful relationship began to attract the attention of national marketing firms and network television executives such as New York TV distributor Sandy Frank. Frank was a top marketer of TV programs nationwide who would soon play an important role in broadening the Buckaroo 500 viewership. Buck, Pom Pom, and Dixie were about to ride into the "Big Apple," the largest television market in the world.

Based on the momentum of its California ratings, Buckaroo 500 was set to try its luck in the large East coast television markets. The

• *Pom Pom, Dixie, and Buck turned out to be naturals at TV marketing. Here Dixie helps out during an ARDEN all-Jersey milk commercial on location in California.*

show's wholesome, informal conglomeration of kids and performing animal stars was to be exposed to urban, East Coast children, many of whom had never seen a farm or many of the farm animals on the Buckaroo 500 TV show.

Even though television executives were convinced that Buckaroo 500's entertaining, character-building approach would be a major positive factor, the pleasant surprise that Buck, Pom Pom, and Dixie had an innate gift for promoting sponsor's products was not lost on East Coast marketing firms.

In the early days of Buckaroo 500's development, Buck had wisely retained the rights to the program by a special arrangement with San Jose station manager Bob Hosfeldt. Weaver strongly believed that the program would be a success, and in exchange for the local station producing segments, he enthusiastically marketed the program himself, securing the station's continued support for the concept. Though a rancher who was unschooled in Madison Avenue

• *Piggly Wiggly supermarkets sponsored Buckaroo 500 on TV stations throughout Texas. Here Buck congratulates a shopping spree winner. (Below right) The Piggly Wiggly brochure helped promote many Buckaroo 500 personalized products.*

• Pom Pom and Buck give a "little wrangler" a ride. Buckaroo 500 went on to become the first successful independently bartered TV show in national syndication. (Below left) Kathy, Chuck, and Jet Jet the Pomeranian look on while Buck feeds an animal guest and Dixie sings. (Below right) Buck bottle-feeds an orphaned colt he adopted while in the background, Chuck helps Mig take care of her daughter.

marketing techniques, Weaver had a natural instinct for promotion.

So, apparently, did Pom Pom, Dixie, and Alex the rooster, whose amusing crows of approval (on command) at the mention of original sponsor Wonder Bread became a Buckaroo 500 staple. In a display of committed advertising support, the baking giant early signed on for fifty-two weeks of time spanning 104 episodes of the show. There was no denying the popularity of Buckaroo 500, as Weaver and his animal friends received more response and fan mail than all other KNTV programs combined. The fact that Buck, with his covered wagon and the Buckaroo 500 pony team, made numerous personal appearances at stores and shopping centers greatly enhanced the program's marketing value in the eyes of advertisers and television executives.

As Buckaroo 500 steadily developed a loyal following, it was apparent that there was something special about the Weaver morning program that enchanted the children, pleased their mothers, and sold the sponsor's products. Advertisers recognized the inherent charm of the Buckaroo 500 crew and enthusiastically agreed to sponsor the program, often with the condition that "Buck does the commercial live in the corral."

Since Buck retained ownership of the show and its videotapes, it was possible for him to increase Buckaroo 500's viewership by selling the program to other stations across the country. He would pre-sell the advertising spots to sponsors, then offer the complete finished show to stations in exchange for air time. Buckaroo 500 went on to become the first successful, independently bartered national show in American television.

For example, if a single show contained six available advertising spots, Weaver would pre-sell half the spots to various sponsors, while leaving the other three open for local advertisers in a given market. Since the station would receive a fully produced, ready-to-air show, the arrangement was extremely appealing to television station executives. Buck Weaver, the Nevada rancher, and his animal side-kicks essentially became pioneers in independently-bartered television syndication. The Piggly Wiggly supermarket chain was so impressed by Buckaroo 500's phenomenal ratings that it purchased the rights to the show for the entire state of Texas.

Sandy Frank, a New York-based marketer of television programs

• (Left) Legendary fastball pitcher, Eddie Feigner, of the King and his Court, was one of Buckaroo 500's celebrity guests. In a phenomenal - barn-storming career, Feigner pitched in 10,127 games, winning 9,743 with 141,517 strikeouts. Of his numerous victories, 930 wins were no-hitters. He struck out a total of 8,698 batters while pitching blindfolded. Feigner is seen here receiving a gift of Tony Lama boots during a guest appearance on Buckaroo 500. (Below) Pom Pom takes a bow in a TV Guide promotional ad.

Watch
BUCKAROO 500
© 1965 BUCK WEAVER
Starring POM POM

When Pom, the trained stallion, Dixie, the World's smartest Doberman, Buck and his Buckaroos get together on Buck's ranch, wonderful fun things always happen.

00:00 AM
ON CH. XX

• (Below) Popular comedian/singer, José Gonzales Gonzales, was discovered on the Groucho Marx show and appeared in numerous movies with John Wayne. He is seen below clowning around with Buck and Pom Pom during a record promotion.

• (Above) A 4-H member appears on the show with a seeing-eye guide dog in training.

nationwide, recognized the show's track record and momentum and acquired distribution rights to Buckaroo 500. Around this time, the Bliss-Grunewald advertising agency was looking for the right marketing tool for one of its clients—Connecticut-based Cocoa Marsh, a milk flavoring produced by the Taylor-Reed Corporation. The agency recommended Buckaroo 500 as the proper vehicle to promote Cocoa Marsh, and the company decided to put Buck Weaver and his wranglers to the test in Manhattan's frenzied TV market. The program was to air on WPIX, the largest independent TV station in the nation at the time.

Arranging programs with Sandy Frank, the station aired the San Jose produced Buckaroo 500 from 12:45 to 1:00 p.m. Monday through Friday, and on a rotating basis between 9 a.m. and noon on Sunday. They had been successful in Western markets, but how would the cowboy host, Pom Pom, Dixie, and their corral of farm animals do in the intense television atmosphere of New York City—America's media capital? Would a city of concrete and steel, lined with towering skyscrapers, filled with intense traffic jams and millions of busy people scurrying like ants through crowed streets, even notice Buckaroo 500? Would those urban children, surrounded by the "hustle and bustle" that personifies New York, relate to the down-home Buckaroo 500 show?

You bet they would!

In short order, Buckaroo 500 began knocking the competition for a loop. Beginning each show with his customary, "Hi, Buckaroos!" Weaver soon doubled his viewing audience in a few short weeks. Taylor-Reed board chairman, Malcolm Taylor, was delighted. In a letter to distributor Sandy Frank, he wrote: "In the twenty-six years of our corporate life, we have participated in many television shows. I am happy to inform you that Buckaroo 500 is already, in its first month over station WPIX-TV, setting a record of performance second to none."

Taylor-Reed was also delighted to receive 27,000 responses, accompanied by Cocoa Marsh "proof-of-purchase" coupons, from a televised Buckaroo 500 offer—1,300 in the first week alone! The energized board chairman encouraged Sandy Frank to secure television time for Buckaroo 500 in as many markets as possible east of St. Louis. In eight weeks, the show was scheduled in twenty-six markets.

New York's WPIX was excited about its new children's program. Station manager Fred M. Thrower commented in a letter to advertising executive Ted Grunewald: "WPIX has been one of the most successful television stations in the country with children's programming for a number of years, and we undoubtedly have the largest library of children's fare in existence. One thing we don't have is something like Buckaroo 500. It is completely unique and different. . . . We quickly realized that Buck Weaver is one of those one-in-a-million personalities who knows how to work with children—in his case, in a most unusual and exciting way. . . . I think that children are going to have so much respect for Weaver that when he tells them to do something, they are going to want to do it."

As one newspaper aptly described it, Buckaroo 500 was "spreading like the measles."

Immediately following their successful New York debut Buck, Pom Pom, Dixie, and the wranglers rode the airwaves into Philadelphia's market with Cocoa Marsh and station WFIL. After the first four weeks, they had already tied the Today Show in the ratings. "Buckaroo 500 is spreading like a prairie fire," an industry publication stated. Soon Pom Pom and the corral crew were being carried by television stations in twenty-eight markets including Chicago, Pittsburgh, Buffalo, Albany, Providence, New Haven, and Charlotte, as well as New York City and Philadelphia. The show caught on in Denver and Portland, as well as securing its large sponsorship by Piggly Wiggly supermarkets for wide exposure on Texas TV stations.

Buckaroo 500 was still operating out of KNTV in San Jose, California where all the show's videotaping took place, but eastern children readily identified with the program. Boys and girls from

• (Below left) Animals are always the stars on Buckaroo 500. Here "Jimmy Jo", a Grand National Livestock Exposition Grand Champian wether lamb pays a visit.

Buffalo, New York wrote WPIX requesting audience tickets, expecting to see a live local episode.

Buck, Joan, and their four children—Mike, Chuck, Tim, and Kathy—had now moved to San Jose. Yet they still maintained a ranch lifestyle, rising at 6:00 a.m. as usual with animal care the first order of each day. On the two-and-a-half-acre home site, perched on a hill overlooking San Jose, the Weavers maintained six horses that appeared regularly on Buckaroo 500. Goats, chickens, several cows, a raccoon, and a pet owl-faced monkey rounded out the animal entourage. Of course the king and queen of this realm were Pom Pom and Dixie.

The children in the eastern cities loved Pom Pom as much as did the "little wranglers" back in the West. Kathy and Buck had trained Pom Pom well. They had come such a long way from the days back in Nevada when the stallion had stuck his head through the bedroom window and introduced himself to a sick little girl. (see p.42) Pom Pom would delight children and adults alike with his humorous nods, mischievous pranks, and his "mathematical wizardry"— solving problems and counting out the answers with his hooves.

Buck was always quick to point out that the Welsh wonder stallion was one of those rare horses that "can sit directly from a standing position, much like a dog. Ninety-nine percent of horses can't do that," Buck still proudly states, and the unusual sight of Pom Pom easing his large frame into that position while patiently viewing the corral proceedings was truly memorable.

Across the country, parents and children often sat together viewing the program with its subtle, positive education. Though the program capitalized on the widely popular Western theme, life with the animals was always natural to Buck. To the show's credit it never

• *(Below left) Two 4-H Club girls accompany guest canines from the San Raphael, California Seeing-Eye Dog School. (Center) Buck and one of Pom's foals. (Right) Dr. Kay Bewley, a San Jose veternarian, appeared weekly with tips on animal care.*

resorted to gunplay or violence, as much television programming tends to do. Though over the years Buck, Pom, and Dixie sold train-loads of Wonder Bread and Cocoa Marsh flavoring (not to mention many other products), they had accomplished something far more meaningful. Amidst the humorous antics and sometimes orchestrated chaos of the Buckaroo 500 corral, millions of "little wranglers" across the United State gleaned positive lessons about life, respect, and responsibility.

The playful shenanigans of Buck and his animals had always been entertaining, but the undertone of the program was still rooted in the philosophy of the Weaver's Nevada Youth Ranch. During those years, hundreds of troubled boys, mostly delinquents, orphans, and products of broken homes, had found their way to the Weaver Ranch. Buck had taught them responsibility through the care of the ranch's horses and livestock. A type of "animal therapy" was developed—a theory later discovered and popularized by child psychologists for helping disturbed children.

This was no new theory to Buck Weaver and his horse-loving daughter Kathy.

They had no psychology degrees, but they had long known about that special chemistry between children and animals. They knew that it was a bond for good, a vehicle by which life's lessons could be taught. Buck has never minded taking a back seat to Pom Pom and Dixie or the many animals that made up Buckaroo 500.

Television executives and parents alike noted the subtle, yet deliberate, principles woven into Buckaroo 500, pointing out the insistence that children "be considerate of animals, as well as people," safety hints, country information that was new to city children, respect, optimism, character, and responsibility And as Alex, Buck's trustworthy bantam rooster, was quick to acknowledge, "Good behavior is always something to crow about."

Yes, Buckaroo 500 really did outrank Leave it to Beaver, The Rifleman, Truth or Consequences, leading soap operas, and the ABC Evening News during a thriving golden era of American television. Yet, that wasn't the show's most important contribution. It's major contribution was reflected in the thousands of gold-and-brown Buckaroo 500 Club pledge cards signed by thousands of children throughout the country and in the lessons they learned behind the antics of a cowboy host, a jaunty Welsh Stallion, and their Doberman side-kick.

Part way through the program's six-year run, the original Pom Pom, though only nine years of age and still a master prankster, suddenly became ill and died. The devastating loss hit the Weaver family and their television friends hard. The Veterinarian School at the University of California (Davis) did an autopsy on the TV wonder stallion, but never could confirm a specific cause of death.

Another similar stallion took Pom Pom's place, but Buck still has a special place in his heart for the original Pom—his old side-kick. "No horse could match his intelligence and personality," Weaver has said. In a period of self-reflection, Buck felt that there was a lesson in Pom Pom's sudden death. Somewhere along the way, in the hectic pace of those years, he knew he had drifted from the faith that had meant so much to him. Maybe, this was somehow a message, a wake-up call. Westerners will tell you that the measure of a man is shown after he's thrown from his horse. A true cowboy dusts himself off and gets right back on. Buck took a self-inventory and again set his priorities straight.

By 1969, Buckaroo 500 (then being produced in San Diego) ended a pioneering, very successful stint in television syndication, and Buck went into business selling advertising. But let's fast-forward our story to December, 2000 . . .

Buck Weaver has asked me to meet him at the Boise airport; he's flying in from Las Vegas, Nevada and wants to check on the manuscript progress for the update of the book you hold in your hands—Pom Pom: The Rest of the Story. As befits a former Golden Gloves boxing champion, the silver-haired Weaver is clad in a tri-colored workout suit and athletic sneakers. These days he

• *TV sidekicks: Buck and Pom Pom. The cowboy host gets a thank-you kiss from the Wonder Stallion.*

dresses either in athletic gear or in classy hand-made cowboy boots, bolo ties, and western wear. I've never seen him dressed in anything else. The cowboy host has lost none of his energy or spirit. The next evening Weaver, a devoted racquetball player who always travels with two racquets, challenges me to a game at a local athletic club.

Though I was still in elementary school when Buckaroo 500 first aired on television, by the end of our match I'm drenched in sweat and at the losing end of a 15-3 score! Buck Weaver is hardly sweating, appearing as if he'd simply been out walking his dog around the block.

I recall our phone conversation a few days previous . . .

"I'm thinking of reviving the show," Buck's enthusiastic voice comes clearly over the phone lines, "I just bought a new Welsh Stallion . . . looks just like Pom Pom . . has that same intelligence . . . he's out at the ranch now . . . I've been working with him."

I smile approvingly to myself. Though I've known Weaver only a short time, I've realized he's an original. He gets things done; he's innovative and tireless, with an unending work ethic.

"I still get up early every morning, sometimes at 3:30 a.m.," Buck tells me. "That way I can get twenty-five hours in a day—by getting up an hour before the day starts!"

Perhaps today's kids need a Buckaroo 500. In this fast-paced society of pulsing lights, action heroes, and a barrage of violence-packed video games pounding at young minds—perhaps there are still some lessons to be learned in the old corral.

• *Fast forward to Las Vegas in 2001: Buck Weaver training the new Pom Pom.*

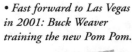

NEW STARS
FROM BUCK'S RANCH

•*The new Pom Pom, a two-year-old Welsh Stallion, in training.*

• "Say-No," an eight-year-old registered Welsh Stallion, also being "highschooled."

• Top: "Say-No" ("Say-No to drugs") exercising at the ranch.

• Right: Buck gets a kiss from the new Pom Pom.

• Insert: "Pom-too," the new Pom Pom's six-hour-old son, learns to smile.

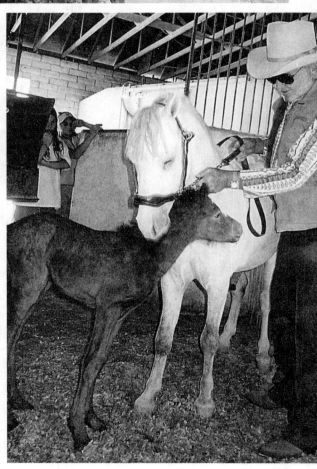

• Top: Shown here at just six hours old, little "Pom-too" gets aquainted with his Mother (Stormie) and Pom II (half brother to Pom).

• Above: Pom being introduced to his new son (Pom-too).

• Right: Pom and Pom-too. . . admiration.

CATCHING UP WITH KATHY

Kathy Weaver Mickelson is still crazy about horses!

Kathy today with Alfredo, her Spanish Arabian stallion.

Kathy Mickelson will tell you herself the best thing about her chilhhood was being raised with a love for the Lord and a passion for horses. She is grateful to her parents for both. She has never wavered in her love of horses. She started riding at the age of three. And yes, she is still crazy about horses. "I believe," says Kathy, "my love of horses is truly a gift from God. I learn so much from the horses—I feel they teach me more than I teach them."

Kathy is versed in several riding disciplines, but her passion lies in the art of "Dressage," one of the most difficult and challenging riding disciplines to master.

"The main thing that has changed since I was a kid," states Kathy, "is that I'm happily married with a wonderful husband and a great career." Since 1987, she has owned and operated her own successful advertising corporation in suburban Salt Lake City, Utah. She operates her growing company from home . . . a two acre "horse heaven." This enables her to work, live, and pursue the equestrian arts in one convenient location. There she tends to her herd of five loving equine friends:

- *Alfredo*—a chestnut Spanish Arabian stallion.
- *Frankie*—a beautiful gray thoroughbred mare.
- *Dartanian*—a Thoroughbred/Andalusion cross (Frankie's son).
- *Mary*—a miniture gelding.
- *Gideon*—a miniture gelding (Mary's son).
- She also has a sassy Jack Russell Terrier named *Zorro* and a cat named *Buster*.

Kathy feels very grateful and blessed to be leading the life she has deamed of. She has a second company, *Equishow Productions Inc.,* that specializes in producing educational videos and television projects in the horse industry.

- *Frankie and Dartanian relaxing in the shade.*

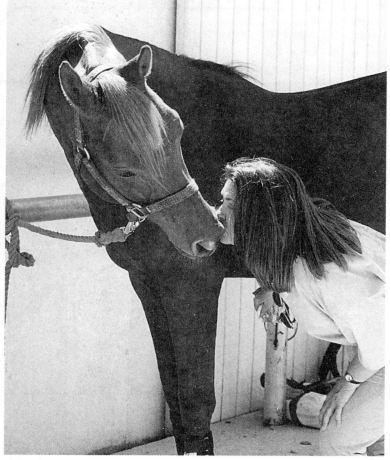

• *Kathy's love of horses has become a rewarding career.*
• *Below: Alfredo strikes a noble pose.*

BUCKAROO 500

DEVOTION	PERFECT SCORE	YOUR SCORE
Church Attendance	75	
Reverence	25	
Daily Prayers	50	
Grace	50	
CHARACTER		
Obedient	20	
Pure	20	
True	20	
Kind	20	
Respectful	20	
Attentive	20	
Helpful	20	
Cheerful	20	
Thoughtful	20	
HEALTH HABITS		
Cleanliness	20	
Hands & Face	20	
Fingernails	20	
Hair Combed	20	
Teeth Brushed	20	
Shoes Shined	20	
TOTAL	**500**	

PLEDGE
"I WILL ALWAYS DO MY BEST"

SIGNATURE

BUCKAROO 500

NAME _____

ADDRESS _____

CITY _____ STATE _____

NOTIFY _____

IN EMERGENCY